100 PLUS
AMERICAN POEMS

Edited by PAUL MOLLOY

Illustrated with photographs selected from the
Scholastic-Kodak Photography Awards 1964-1978.

SCHOLASTIC INC.
New York Toronto London Auckland Sydney

ISBN 0-590-42698-2

12 11 10 9 8 7 6

Printed in the U.S.A.

4/9

28

Robert Bly for "A Missouri Traveller Writes Home: 1830," © 1957 by Robert Bly, and "Driving Toward the Lac Qui Parle River," © 1962 by Robert Bly, from SILENCE IN THE SNOWY FIELDS by Robert Bly, published by Wesleyan University Press.

Julian Bond, Member of the Georgia House of Representatives, for "The Bishop of Atlanta: Ray Charles" by Julian Bond.

Curtis Brown, Ltd. for "The Sleeping Giant" by Donald Hall, © 1955 by Donald Hall.

Coward-McCann, Inc. for "Calling In The Cat" and "The Mouse Complains" from COMPASS ROSE by Elizabeth Coatsworth, copyright 1929 by Coward-McCann, Inc.; renewed 1957 by Elizabeth Coatsworth.

J. M. Dent & Sons, Ltd. for British Commonwealth rights, excluding Canada, to "Edouard," "Lama," "The Purist," "A Caution to Everybody," and "Requiem" by Ogden Nash.

Doubleday & Co., Inc., for "the coming of archie," "mehitabel was once cleopatra," "the lesson of the moth," and "the hen and the oriole" from ARCHY AND MEHITABEL by Don Marquis, copyright 1927 by Doubleday & Co., Inc.; "The Bat," copyright 1939 by Theodore Roethke; "The Pike," copyright © 1963 by Beatrice Roethke as Administratrix of the Estate of Theodore Roethke; "Child on Top of a Greenhouse," copyright 1946 Editorial Publications, Inc. All from THE COLLECTED POEMS OF THEODORE ROETHKE.

Norma Millay Ellis for "Counting-Out Rhyme" by Edna St. Vincent Millay from COLLECTED POEMS, published by Harper & Row, Publishers. Copyrights 1928, 1955 by Edna St. Vincent Millay and Norma Millay Ellis.

Faber and Faber Ltd. for British Commonwealth rights to: "The Bat," "The Pike" and "Child on Top of a Greenhouse" by Theodore Roethke; "The Pardon," "Digging for China," "Mind," the first three lines of "Potato" (titled "Blind Vegetable" herein) the first three stanzas from "Running" by Richard Wilbur; "Elegy for J.F.K." and "O Where Are You Going" by W. H. Auden.

Victor Gollancz Ltd. for British Commonwealth rights to "Capacity" by John Updike.

Harcourt, Brace & World, Inc., for "Arithmetic" and "Phizzog" by Carl Sandburg from GOOD MORNING, AMERICA, copyright 1928, 1956 by Carl Sandburg, "Dog at Night" by Louis Untermeyer, copyright 1928 by Harcourt, Brace & World, Inc., renewed 1956 by Louis Untermeyer. Reprinted from his volume, LONG FEUD; first three lines of "Potato" (titled "Blind Vegetable" herein) by Richard Wilbur from THE BEAUTIFUL CHANGES, copyright 1947 by Richard Wilbur; "Digging for China" and "Mind" by Richard Wilbur from THINGS OF THIS WORLD, © 1956 by Richard Wilbur; "The Pardon" by Richard Wilbur from CEREMONY AND OTHER POEMS, copyright 1948, 1949, 1950 by Richard Wilbur; first three stanzas of "Running" by Richard Wilbur, © 1968 by Richard Wilbur. Reprinted from his volume, WALKING TO SLEEP. First published in The New Yorker.

Harper & Row, Publishers for "Incident" from ON THESE I STAND by Countee Cullen, copyright 1925 by Harper & Brothers, renewed 1953 by Ida M. Cullen; "Mouse Night: One of Our Games" (1959) from TRAVELING

CONTENTS

GROUP I
SONGS OF INNOCENCE & EXPERIENCE

GROUP II
QUADRUPEDS & OTHER CREATURES

GROUP III
PEOPLE & PLACES

GROUP IV
THE FIRST AMERICANS

GROUP V
WITH A MORAL SPOKEN OR UNSPOKEN

GROUP VI
THE PLAY OF WORDS

GROUP VII
RIDDLES TO UNRIDDLE

FOREWORD

A young friend who likes poetry has assured me that he never reads forewords. To be brief then, in this aside to stray older readers, let's remind ourselves that often we forget how much of our own liking for poetry began with the enjoyment of bad poems — bad in the sense of easy and obvious: popular songs, folk ballads, verse often close to doggerel. There are multitudes of good "bad" poems, and we need not keep secret our fondness for some of them. Nor should we deprive new readers of equal opportunities to explore and enjoy poetry that may be more difficult and even positively mystifying. Frost was in his ninth decade when he confessed he did not understand Emerson's "Uriel" until he was eighty. Nothing that puzzling here, but there *are* half a dozen poems of more than average difficulty, usually the last one in each section.

The heading for the opening group, "Songs of Innocence and Experience," echoes the titles of William Blake's two volumes of lyrics. The words *innocence* and *experience*, however, are intended less to represent the opposites Blake was balancing against each other (belief against doubt; confidence and vision against despair) than they are intended to suggest the deeply felt, often bewildering, sometimes joyful, moments of childhood and youth that later the poet, remembering, recreates with new meaning.

"The Play of Words," Group Six, gathers poems that in a number of ways reflect nearly every poet's exuberant love of language: in the interplay of wit and metaphor, in the vitality of American speech, in fresh description, in new and unexpected rhymes. And the final group, "Riddles to Unriddle," offers the pure fun of mystification—with all the answers in the notes at the back.

Besides the range from easy to difficult poems, I've tried to link early American poets like Freneau and Whittier with recent ones like Sandburg and Nash and Swenson, to join the most concerned moral teachers with the most light-hearted word jugglers. And in the work of black poets like Langston Hughes and Countee Cullen and in the Indian poems of Peter LaFarge and William Stafford I hope young people will find both those relating to the present and those that reveal America's past.

Paul Molloy

Gene Cooper, El Camino Real High School, Woodland Hills, CA

I
Songs of Innocence
& Experience

DREAM BOOGIE

Good morning daddy!
Ain't you heard
The boogie-woogie rumble
Of a dream deferred?

Listen closely:
You'll hear their feet
Beating out and beating out a —

You think
It's a happy beat?

Listen to it closely:
Ain't you heard
something underneath
like a —

What did I say?

Sure,
I'm happy!
Take it away!

Hey, pop!
Re-bop!
Mop

Y-e-a-h!

Langston Hughes

FIFTEEN

South of the Bridge on Seventeenth
I found back of the willows one summer
day a motorcycle with engine running
as it lay on its side, ticking over
slowly in the high grass.   I was fifteen.

I admired all that pulsing gleam, the
shiny flanks, the demure headlights
fringed where it lay; I led it gently
to the road and stood with that
companion, ready and friendly.   I was fifteen.

We could find the end of a road, meet
the sky on out Seventeenth. I thought about
hills, and patting the handle got back a
confident opinion. On the bridge we indulged
a forward feeling, a tremble.   I was fifteen.

Thinking, back farther in the grass I found
the owner, just coming to, where he had flipped
over the rail. He had blood on his hand, was pale —
I helped him walk to his machine. He ran his hand
over it, called me good man, roared away.

I stood there, fifteen.

William Stafford

A PECK OF GOLD

(as of about 1880)

Dust always blowing about the town,
Except when sea-fog laid it down,
And I was one of the children told
Some of the blowing dust was gold.

All the dust the wind blew high
Appeared like gold in the sunset sky,
But I was one of the children told
Some of the dust was really gold.

Such was life in the Golden Gate:
Gold dusted all we drank and ate,
And I was one of the children told,
"We all must eat our peck of gold."

Robert Frost

From RUNNING

What were we playing? Was it prisoner's base?
I ran with whacking keds
Down the cart-road past Rickard's place,
And where it dropped beside the tractor-sheds

Leapt out into the air above a blurred
Terrain, through jolted light,
Took two hard lopes, and at the third
Spanked off a hummock-side exactly right,

And made the turn, and with delighted strain
Sprinted across the flat
By the bull-pen and up the lane.
Thinking of happiness, I think of that.

Richard Wilbur

DIGGING FOR CHINA

"Far enough down is China," somebody said.
"Dig deep enough and you might see the sky
As clear as at the bottom of a well.
Except it would be a real — a different sky.
Then you could burrow down until you came
To China! Oh, it's nothing like New Jersey.
There's people, trees, and houses, and all that,
But much, much different. Nothing looks the same."

I went and got the trowel out of the shed
And sweated like a coolie all that morning,
Digging a hole beside the lilac bush,
Down on my hands and knees. It was a sort
Of praying, I suspect. I watched my hand
Dig deep and darker, and I tried and tried
To dream a place where nothing was the same.
The trowel never did break through to blue.

Before the dream could weary of itself
My eyes were tired of looking into darkness.
My sunbaked head of hanging down a hole.
I stood up in a place I had forgotten,
Blinking and staggering while the earth went round
And showed me silver barns, the fields dozing
In palls of brightness, patens growing and gone
In the tides of leaves, and the whole sky china blue.
Until I got my balance back again
All that I saw was China, China, China.

Richard Wilbur

THE SLEEPING GIANT
(A Hill, So Named, in Hamden, Connecticut)

The whole day long, under the walking sun
That poised an eye on me from its high floor,
Holding my toy beside the clapboard house
I looked for him, the summer I was four.

I was afraid the waking arm would break
From the loose earth and rub against his eyes
A fist of trees, and the whole country tremble
In the exultant labor of his rise;

Then he with giant steps in the small streets
Would stagger, cutting off the sky, to seize
The roofs from house and home because we had
Covered his shape with dirt and planted trees;

And then kneel down and rip with fingernails
A trench to pour the enemy Atlantic
Into our basin, and the water rush,
With the streets full and the voices frantic.

That was the summer I expected him.
Later the high and watchful sun instead
Walked low behind the house, and school began,
And winter pulled a sheet over his head.

Donald Hall

CHILD ON TOP OF A GREENHOUSE

The wind billowing out of the seat of my britches,
My feet crackling splinters of glass and dried putty,
The half-grown chrysanthemums staring up like ac-
    cusers,
Up through the streaked glass, flashing with sunlight,
A few white clouds all rushing eastward,
A line of elms plunging and tossing like horses,
And everyone, everyone pointing up and shouting!

Theodore Roethke

TO THE SNAKE

Green Snake, when I hung you round my neck
and stroked your cold, pulsing throat
    as you hissed to me, glinting
arrowy gold scales, and I felt
    the weight of you on my shoulders,
and the whispering silver of your dryness
    sounded close at my ears —

Green Snake — I swore to my companions that
    certainly you were harmless! But truly
I had no certainty, and no hope, only desiring
    to hold you, for that joy,
                            which left
a long wake of pleasure, as the leaves moved
and you faded into the pattern
of grass and shadows, and I returned
smiling and haunted, to a dark morning.

Denise Levertov

I, TOO

I, too, sing America.

I am the darker brother.
They send me to eat in the kitchen
When company comes,
But I laugh,
And eat well,
And grow strong.

Tomorrow,
I'll sit at the table
When company comes.
Nobody'll dare
Say to me,
"Eat in the kitchen,"
Then.

Besides,
They'll see how beautiful I am
And be ashamed —

I, too, am America.

Langston Hughes

INCIDENT

Once riding in old Baltimore,
   Heart-filled, head-filled with glee,
I saw a Baltimorean
   Keep looking straight at me.

Now I was eight and very small,
   And he was no whit bigger,
And so I smiled, but he poked out
   His tongue and called me, "Nigger."

I saw the whole of Baltimore
   From May until December:
Of all the things that happened there
   That's all that I remember.

Countee Cullen

Lawrence Melkus, Fitzgerald Jr.-Sr. High School, Warren, Mich.

LITTLE SONG

Carmencita loves Patrick.
Patrick loves Si Lan Chen.
Xenophon loves Mary Jane.
Hildegarde loves Ben.

Lucienne loves Eric.
Giovanni loves Emma Lee.
Natasha loves Miguelito —
And Miguelito loves me.

Ring around the Maypole!
Ring around we go —
Weaving our bright ribbons
Into a rainbow!

Langston Hughes

21

THE HIGH SCHOOL BAND

On warm days in September the high school band
Is up with the birds and marches along our street,
Boom boom,
To a field where it goes boom boom until eight forty-
    five
When it marches, as in the old rhyme, back, boom
    boom,
To its study halls, leaving our street
Empty except for the leaves that descend, to no drum,
And lie still.
In September
A great many high school bands beat a great many
    drums,
And the silences after their partings are very deep.

Reed Whittemore

THE BLUE TAIL FLY

When I was young I used to wait
On my master and serve him his plate,
And pass the bottle when he got dry
And brush away the Blue Tail Fly.

   Jimmy cracked corn and I don't care
   Jimmy cracked corn and I don't care
   Jimmy cracked corn and I don't care
   My master's gone away.

And when he'd ride in the afternoon
I'd follow with a hickory broom,
The pony being rather shy
When bitten by the Blue Tail Fly.

One day he rode around the farm
The flys so numerous they did swarm,
One chanced to bite him on the thigh
The devil take a Blue Tail Fly.

The pony jump, he toss, he pitch
He threw my master in the ditch,
He died and the jury wondered why
The verdict was the Blue Tail Fly.

He lies beneath a 'simmon tree
His epitaph is there to see:
"Beneath this stone I'm forced to lie;
The victim of a Blue Tail Fly."

Anonymous

MOTHER TO SON

Well, son, I'll tell you:
Life for me ain't been no crystal stair.
It's had tacks in it,
And splinters,
And boards torn up,
And places with no carpet on the floor —
Bare.
But all the time
I'se been a-climbin' on,
And reachin' landin's,
And turnin' corners,
And sometimes goin' in the dark
Where there ain't been no light.
So boy, don't you turn back.
Don't you set down on the steps
'Cause you finds it's kinder hard.
Don't you fall now —
For I'se still goin', honey,
I'se still climbin',
And life for me ain't been no crystal stair.

Langston Hughes

ELEVEN

And summer mornings the mute child, rebellious,
Stupid, hating the words, the meanings, hating
The Think now, Think, the O but Think! would leave
On tiptoe the three chairs on the verandah
And crossing tree by tree the empty lawn
Push back the shed door and upon the sill
Stand pressing out the sunlight from his eyes
And enter and with outstretched fingers feel
The grindstone and behind it the bare wall
And turn and in the corner on the cool
Hard earth sit listening. And one by one,
Out of the dazzled shadow in the room,
The shapes would gather, the brown plowshare, spades,
Mattocks, the polished helves of picks, a scythe
Hung from the rafters, shovels, slender tines
Glinting across the curve of sickles — shapes
Older than men were, the wise tools, the iron
Friendly with earth. And sit there, quiet, breathing
The harsh dry smell of withered bulbs, the faint
Odor of dung, the silence. And outside
Beyond the half-shut door the blind leaves
And the corn moving. And at noon would come,
Up from the garden, his hard crooked hands
Gentle with earth, his knees still earth-stained, smelling
Of sun, of summer, the old gardener, like
A priest, like an interpreter, and bend
Over his baskets.
                    And they would not speak:
They would say nothing. And the child would sit there
Happy as though he had no name, as though
He had been no one: like a leaf, a stem,
Like a root growing —

                                        Archibald MacLeish

25

Paul Lierhaus, Kent (Ohio) Roosevelt High School

THE DAY TIME BEGAN

Our days were yellow and green
we marked the seasons with respect,
but spring was ours. We were shoots
and sprouts, and greenings,
We heard the first word
that fish were running in the creek.
Secretive we went with men into sheds
for torches and tridents
for nets and traps.
We shared the wildness of that week,
in men and fish. First fruits
after the winter. Dried meat gone,
the pork barrel holding only brine.
Bank clerks came out in skins,
teachers in loin clouts,
while game wardens drove in darkened cars,
watching the vagrant flares
beside the fish mad streams, or crouched
at home to see who came and went,
holding their peace
surprised by violence.

We were spendthrift of time
A day was not too much to spend
to find a willow right for a whistle
to blow the greenest sound the world
has ever heard.
Another day to search the oak and hickory thickets,
geometry and experience run together
to choose the fork, fit
for a sling.
Whole days long we pursued the spotted frogs
and dared the curse of newts and toads.

New Adams, unhurried, pure, we checked the names
given by the old.
Some things we found well titled
blood-root for sight
skunks for smell
crab apples for taste
yarrow for sound
mallow for touch.
Some we found named ill, too little or too much
or in a foreign tongue.
These we challenged with new names.

Space was our preoccupation,
infinity, not eternity our concern.
We were strong bent on counting,
the railroad ties, so many to a mile,
the telephone poles, the cars that passed,
marking our growth against the door frames.

The sky was a kite,
I flew it on a string,
winding it in to see its blue, again
to count the whirling swallows,
and read the patterned scroll of blackbirds turning
to check the marking of the hawk,
and then letting it out to the end
of the last pinched inch of
string, in the vise of thumb and finger.

One day the string broke,
the kite fled over the shoulder of the world,
but reluctantly, reaching back in great lunges
as lost kites do, or as a girl running

in a reversed movie, as at each arched step, the earth
set free, leaps forward, catching her farther back
the treadmill doubly betraying,
Remote and more remote.

Now I lie on a west facing hill in October
the dragging string having circled the world,
   the universe,
crosses my hand in the grass. I do not grasp it,
it brushes my closed eyes, I do not open.
That world is no longer mine, but for remembrance
Space ended then, and time began.

Eugene McCarthy

THE PARDON

My dog lay dead five days without a grave
In the thick of summer, hid in a clump of pine
And a jungle of grass and honeysuckle vine.
I who had loved him while he kept alive

Went only close enough to where he was
To sniff the heavy honeysuckle-smell
Twined with another odor heavier still
And hear the flies' intolerable buzz.

Well, I was ten and very much afraid.
In my kind world the dead were out of range
And I could not forgive the sad or strange
In beast or man. My father took the spade

And buried him. Last night I saw the grass
Slowly divide (it was the same scene
But now it glowed a fierce and mortal green)
And saw the dog emerging.   I confess

I felt afraid again, but still he came
In the carnal sun, clothed in a hymn of flies,
And death was breeding in his lively eyes.
I started in to cry and call his name,

Asking forgiveness of his tongueless head.
. . . I dreamt the past was never past redeeming:
But whether this was false or honest dreaming
I beg death's pardon now. And mourn the dead.

Richard Wilbur

AT MIDNIGHT'S HOUR I RAISED
MY HEAD

At midnight's hour I raised my head,
The owls were seeking for their bread;
The foxes barked impatient still,
At their wan fate they bear so ill. —
I thought me of eternities delayed
And of commands but half obeyed. —
The night wind rustled through the glade
As if a force of men there staid;
The word was whispered through the ranks
And every hero seized his lance;
The word was whispered through the ranks,
    Advance.

Henry David Thoreau

Peggy Reynolds, West High School, Phoenix, Ariz.

THE LONG VOYAGE

Not that the pines were darker there,
nor mid-May dogwood brighter there,
nor swifts more swift in summer air;
   It was my own country,

having its thunderclap of spring,
its long midsummer ripening,
its corn hoar-stiff at harvesting,
   almost like any country,

yet being mine; its face, its speech,
its hill bent low within my reach,
its river birch and upland beech
   were mine, of my own country.

Now the dark waters at the bow
fold back, like earth against the plow;
foam brightens like the dogwood now
   at home, in my own country.

Malcolm Cowley

Susan King, Reseda High School, Reseda, CA

MY LOST YOUTH

Often I think of the beautiful town
That is seated by the sea;
Often in thought go up and down
The pleasant streets of that dear old town,
    And my youth comes back to me.
      And a verse of a Lapland song
      Is haunting my memory still:
      "A boy's will is the wind's will,
And the thoughts of youth are long, long thoughts."

I can see the shadowy lines of its trees,
    And catch, in sudden gleams,
The sheen of the far-surrounding seas,
And islands that were the Hesperides
    Of all my boyish dreams.
      And the burden of that old song,
      It murmurs and whispers still:
      "A boy's will is the wind's will,
And the thoughts of youth are long, long thoughts."

I remember the black wharves and the slips,
    And the sea-tides tossing free;
And Spanish sailors with bearded lips,
And the beauty and mystery of the ships,
    And the magic of the sea.
      And the voice of that wayward song
      Is singing and saying still:
      "A boy's will is the wind's will,
And the thoughts of youth are long, long thoughts."

I remember the bulwarks by the shore
    And the fort upon the hill;
The sunrise gun, with its hollow roar,

Donald Cameron, Central Jr. High School, Quincy, Mass.

The drumbeat repeated o'er and o'er,
   And the bugle wild and shrill.
      And the music of that old song
      Throbs in my memory still:
      "A boy's will is the wind's will,
And the thoughts of youth are long, long thoughts."

I remember the sea-fight far away,
   How it thundered o'er the tide!
And the dead captains, as they lay
In their graves, o'erlooking the tranquil bay
   Where they in battle died.
      And the sound of that mournful song
      Goes through me with a thrill:
      "A boy's will is the wind's will,
And the thoughts of youth are long, long thoughts."

I can see the breezy dome of groves,
   The shadows of Deering's Woods;
And the friendships old and the early loves
Come back with a Sabbath sound, as of doves
   In quiet neighborhoods.
      And the verse of that sweet old song,
      It flutters and murmurs still:
      "A boy's will is the wind's will,
And the thoughts of youth are long, long thoughts."

I remember the gleams and glooms that dart
   Across the school boy's brain;
The song and the silence in the heart,
That in part are prophecies, and in part
   Are longings wild and vain.
      And the voice of that fitful song
      Sings on, and is never still:
      "A boy's will is the wind's will,
And the thoughts of youth are long, long thoughts."

There are things of which I may not speak;
   There are dreams that cannot die;
There are thoughts that make the strong heart weak,
And bring a pallor into the cheek,
   And a mist before the eye.
     And the words of that fatal song
     Come over me like a chill:
     "A boy's will is the wind's will,
And the thoughts of youth are long, long thoughts."

Strange to me now are the forms I meet
   When I visit the dear old town;
But the native air is pure and sweet,
And the trees that o'ershadow each well-known street,
   As they balance up and down,
     Are singing the beautiful song,
     Are sighing and whispering still:
     "A boy's will is the wind's will,
And the thoughts of youth are long, long thoughts."

And Deering's Woods are fresh and fair,
   And with joy that is almost pain
My heart goes back to wander there,
And among the dreams of the days that were,
   I find my lost youth again.
     And the strange and beautiful song,
     The groves are repeating it still:
     "A boy's will is the wind's will,
And the thoughts of youth are long, long thoughts."

Henry Wadsworth Longfellow

MOWING

There was never a sound beside the wood but one,
And that was my long scythe whispering to the ground.
What was it it whispered? I knew not well myself;
Perhaps it was something about the heat of the sun,
Something, perhaps, about the lack of sound —
And that was why it whispered and did not speak.
It was no dream of the gift of idle hours,
Or easy gold at the hand of fay or elf:
Anything more than the truth would have seemed too
    weak
To the earnest love that laid the swale in rows,
Not without feeble-pointed spikes of flowers
(Pale orchises), and scared a bright green snake.
The fact is the sweetest dream that labor knows.
My long scythe whispered and left the hay to make.

Robert Frost

Dennis Pierce, Santa Monica (Calif.) High School

Stephen Knobloch, DeWitt Clinton High School, Bronx, N.Y.

II

Quadrupeds
& Other Creatures

THE RUNAWAY

Once when the snow of the year was beginning to fall,
We stopped by a mountain pasture to say, "Whose
   colt?"
A little Morgan had one forefoot on the wall,
The other curled at his breast. He dipped his head
And snorted at us. And then he had to bolt,
We heard the miniature thunder where he fled,
And we saw him, or thought we saw him, dim and
   gray,
Like a shadow against the curtain of falling flakes.
"I think the little fellow's afraid of the snow.
He isn't winter broken. It isn't play
With the little fellow at all. He's running away.
I doubt if even his mother could tell him, 'Sakes,
It's only weather.' He'd think she didn't know!
Where is his mother? He can't be out alone."
And now he comes again with a clatter of stone
And mounts the wall again with whited eyes
And all his tail that isn't hair up straight.
He shudders his coat as if to throw off flies.
"Whoever it is that leaves him out so late,
When other creatures have gone to stall and bin,
Ought to be told to come and take him in."

Robert Frost

DOGS AND WEATHER

I'd like a different dog
  For every kind of weather —
A narrow greyhound for a fog,
    A wolfhound strange and white,
  With a tail like a silver feather
    To run with in the night,
      When snow is still, and winter stars
        are bright.

In the fall I'd like to see
  In answer to my whistle,
A golden spaniel look at me.
    But best of all for rain
  A terrier, hairy as a thistle,
    To trot with fine disdain
      Beside me down the soaked, sweet-
        smelling lane.

Winifred Welles

Matt Abrams, South Pasadena High School, South Pasadena, CA

DOG AT NIGHT

At first he stirs uneasily in sleep
And, since the moon does not run off, unfolds
Protesting paws. Grumbling that he must keep
Both eyes awake, he whimpers; then he scolds
And, rising to his feet, demands to know
The stranger's business. You who break the dark
With insolent light, who are you? Where do you go?
But nothing answers his indignant bark.
The moon ignores him, walking on as though
Dogs never were. Stiffened to fury now,
His small hairs stand upright, his howls come fast,
And terrible to hear is his bow-wow
That tears the night. Stirred by this bugle-blast,
The farmer's bitch grows active; without pause
Summons her mastiff and the hound that lies
Three fields away to rally to the cause.
And the next county wakes. And miles beyond
Throats tear themselves and brassy lungs respond
With threats, entreaties, bellowings, and cries,
Chasing the white intruder down the skies.

Louis Untermeyer

Marc Schiff, Cleveland Heights (Ohio) High School

OLD BLUE

I had a dog and his name was Blue.
Bet ya five dollars he's a good one, too.
   Ya — oh Blue, you good dog, you.

Well, I shouldered my ax and I tooted my horn,
Gonna catch me a possum in the new ground corn.
   Ya — oh Blue, you can come, too.

Old Blue's feet was big and round.
He never 'lowed a possum to touch the ground.
   Ya — oh Blue, you're a good dog, you.

Old Blue tree'd; I went to see.
There was a possum in a 'simmon tree.

Well, the possum hung down on a swinging limb.
Blue barked at the possum, possum growled at him.

Blue grinned at me; I smiled at him.
I shook him out and took him in.
   Ya — oh Blue, you good dog, you.

I baked that possum good and brown,
And laid them sweet potatoes round and round.
   Ya — oh Blue, you can have some, too.

Blue, what makes your eyes so red?
You've run them possums till you're almost dead.
   Ya — oh Blue, you good dog, you.

When old Blue died, he died so hard,
He shook the ground in my backyard.

When old Blue died, I laid him in the shade;
I dug his grave with a silver spade.

Lowered him down with a golden chain;
In every link I called his name.
   Ya — oh Blue, you good dog, you.

Well, I'm gonna tell you, so you'll know,
That old Blue's gone where the good dogs go.

But there's just one thing that bothers my mind:
Old Blue went to heaven, left me behind.
   Ya — oh Blue, you good dog, you.

Anonymous

Karen Lukas, Seton High School, Cincinnati, Ohio

CALLING IN THE CAT

Now from the dark, a deeper dark,
the cat slides,
furtive and aware,
his eyes still shine with meteor spark,
the cold dew weights his hair.
Suspicious,
hesitant, he comes
stepping morosely from the night,
held but repelled,
repelled but held,
by lamp and firelight.

Now call your blandest,
offer up
the sacrifice of meat,
and snare the wandering soul with greeds,
give him to drink and eat,
and he shall walk fastidiously
into the trap of old
on feet that still smell delicately
of withered ferns and mold.

Elizabeth Coatsworth

THE SECRET IN THE CAT

I took my cat apart
to see what made him purr.
Like an electric clock
or like the snore

of a warming kettle,
something fizzed and sizzled in him
Was he a soft car,
the engine bubbling sound?

Was there a wire beneath his fur,
or humming throttle?
I undid his throat.
Within was no stir.

I opened his chest
as though it were a door:
no whisk or rattle there.
I lifted off his skull:

no hiss or murmur.
I halved his little belly
but found no gear,
no cause for static.

So I replaced his lid,
laced his little gut.
His heart into his vest I slid
and buttoned up his throat.

James Abrahams, Great Neck North Junior High School, Great Neck, N.Y.

His tail rose to a rod
and beckoned to the air.
Some voltage made him vibrate
warmer than before.

Whiskers and a tail:
perhaps they caught
some radar code
emitted as a pip, a dot-and-dash

of woolen sound.
My cat a kind of tuning fork? —
amplifier? — telegraph? —
doing secret signal work?

His eyes elliptic tubes:
there's a message in his stare.
I stroke him
but cannot find the dial.

May Swenson

THE PASTURE

I'm going out to clean the pasture spring;
I'll only stop to rake the leaves away
(And wait to watch the water clear, I may):
I sha'n't be gone long.   You come too.

I'm going out to fetch the little calf
That's standing by the mother. It's so young
It totters when she licks it with her tongue.
I sha'n't be gone long.   You come too.

Robert Frost

BOBWHITE

Through hottest days the bobwhite sings;
His two-toned, reedy whistle rings
Windblown, familiar on this lawn,
Or to remoter green withdrawn,
At one with evening as with dawn.

His other name, the quail, suggests
Gunshot and slaughter-emptied nests;
The squinting eye, the flabby grin,
As the curst hunter closes in.

Bobwhite — I call him what he calls
Himself, though often he'll repeat
The first of his cool syllables
As though to quench the summer heat —
Small sun-defier, to whose golden
Note my summer is beholden.

Robert Hillyer

THE MOUSE COMPLAINS

I heard a mouse
Bitterly complaining
In a crack of moonlight
Aslant on the floor —

"Little I ask
And that little is not granted.
There are few crumbs
In this world any more.

"The bread-box is tin
And I cannot get in.

"The jam's in a jar
My teeth cannot mar.

"The cheese sits by itself
On the pantry shelf —

"All night I run
Searching and seeking,
All night I run
About on the floor,

"Moonlight is there
And a bare place for dancing,
But no little feast
Is spread any more."

Elizabeth Coatsworth

MOO!

Summer is over, the old cow said,
And they'll shut me up in a draughty shed
To milk me by lamplight in the cold,
But I won't give much for I am old.
It's long ago that I came here
Gay and slim as a woodland deer;
It's long ago that I heard the roar
Of Smith's white bull by the sycamore.
And now there are bones where my flesh should be;
My backbone sags like an old roof tree,
And an apple snatched in a moment's frolic
Is just so many days of colic.
I'm neither a Jersey nor Holstein now
But only a faded sort of cow.
My calves are veal and I had as lief
That I could lay me down as beef;
Somehow, they always kill by halves, —
Why not take me when they take my calves?
Birch turns yellow and sumac red,
I've seen this all before, she said,
I'm tired of the field and tired of the shed
There's no more grass, there's no more clover
Summer is over, summer is over.

Robert Hillyer

WHALE AT TWILIGHT

The sea is enormous, but calm with evening
    and sunset,
rearranging its islands for the night,
    changing its own blues,
smoothing itself against the rocks, without
    playfulness, without thought.
No stars are out, only sea birds flying to
    distant reefs.
No vessels intrude, no lobstermen haul their
    pots.
Only somewhere out toward the horizon a thin
    column of water appears
and disappears again, and then rises once more,
tranquil as a fountain in a garden where no
    wind blows.

Elizabeth Coatsworth

THE PIKE

The river turns,
Leaving a place for the eye to rest,
A furred, a rocky pool,
A bottom of water.

The crabs tilt and eat, leisurely,
And the small fish lie, without shadow, motionless,
Or drift lazily in and out of the weeds.
The bottom-stones shimmer back their irregular
   striations,
And a half-sunken branch bends away from the gazer's
   eye.

A scene for the self to abjure! —
And I lean, almost into the water,
My eye always beyond the surface reflection;
I lean, and love these manifold shapes,
Until, out from a dark cove,
From beyond the end of a mossy log,
With one sinuous ripple, then a rush,
A thrashing-up of the whole pool,
The pike strikes.

Theodore Roethke

I THINK I COULD TURN AND LIVE WITH ANIMALS

I think I could turn and live with animals,
  they are so placid and self-contained;
I stand and look at them long and long.
They do not sweat and whine about their condition;
They do not lie awake in the dark and weep for their
  sins;
They do not make me sick discussing their duty to
  God;
Not one is dissatisfied — not one is demented with the
  mania of owning things;
Not one kneels to another, nor to his kind that lived
  thousands of years ago;
Not one is respectable or industrious over the whole
  earth.

Walt Whitman

H. Cartier-Bresson/Magnum

Dennis Pierce, Santa Monica (Calif.) High School

WHO IS SAD?

Who is sad and who is sorry?
Not the seagull flying high,
not the wren, brown as earth is,
not the bumblebee buzzing by,
not the cat upon the doorstep,
not the dog beside the gate —
they are neither sad nor sorry,
proud, ashamed, on time, nor late.

Elizabeth Coatsworth

THE BAT

By day the bat is cousin to the mouse.
He likes the attic of an aging house.

His fingers make a hat about his head.
His pulse beat is so slow we think him dead.

He loops in crazy figures half the night
Among the trees that face the corner light.

But when he brushes up against a screen,
We are afraid of what our eyes have seen:

For something is amiss or out of place
When mice with wings can wear a human face.

Theodore Roethke

MIND

Mind in its purest play is like some bat
That beats about in caverns all alone,
Contriving by a kind of senseless wit
Not to conclude against a wall of stone.

It has no need to falter or explore;
Darkly it knows what obstacles are there,
And so may weave and flitter, dip and soar
In perfect courses through the blackest air.

And has this simile a like perfection?
The mind is like a bat. Precisely. Save
That in the very happiest intellection
A graceful error may correct the cave.

Richard Wilbur

Lindsay Larson, Murchison Jr. High School, Austin, Texas

Harvey Stein

III

American
Places and People

THE NEGRO SPEAKS OF RIVERS

I've known rivers:
I've known rivers ancient as the world and
   older than the flow of human blood in
   human veins.

My soul has grown deep like the rivers.

I bathed in the Euphrates when dawns were young.
I built my hut near the Congo and it lulled me
   to sleep.
I looked upon the Nile and raised the pyramids
   above it.
I heard the singing of the Mississippi when
   Abe Lincoln went down to New Orleans, and
   I've seen its muddy bosom turn all golden
   in the sunset.

I've known rivers:
Ancient, dusky rivers.

My soul has grown deep like the rivers.

Langston Hughes

Victor Landers, John C. Fremont High School, Los Angeles, CA

LOCALITIES

Wagon Wheel Gap is a place I never saw
And Red Horse Gulch and the chutes of
   Cripple Creek.

Red-shirted miners picking in the sluices,
Gamblers with red neckties in the night streets,
The fly-by-night towns of Bull Frog and Skiddoo,
The night-cool limestone white of Death Valley,
The straight drop of eight hundred feet
From a shelf road in the Hasiampa Valley:
Men and places they are I never saw.

I have seen three White Horse taverns,
One in Illinois, one in Pennsylvania,
One in a timber-hid road of Wisconsin.

I bought cheese and crackers
Between sun showers in a place called White
   Pigeon,
Nestling with a blacksmith shop, a post office,
And a berry-crate factory, where four roads cross.

On the Pecatonica River near Freeport
I have seen boys run barefoot in the leaves
Throwing clubs at the walnut trees
In the yellow-and-gold of autumn,
And there was a brown mash dry on the inside
   of their hands.

On the Cedar Fork Creek of Knox County
I know how the fingers of late October
Loosen the hazel nuts.
I know the brown eyes of half-open hulls.
I know boys named Lindquist, Swanson, Hildebrand.

I remember their cries when the nuts were
   ripe
And some are in machine shops; some are in the
   navy
And some are not on payrolls anywhere.
Their mothers are through waiting for them to
   come home.

Carl Sandburg

Tony Caputo, Reseda High School, Reseda, California

CHICAGO
(as of about 1916)

Hog Butcher for the World,
Tool Maker, Stacker of Wheat,
Player with Railroads and the Nation's
    Freight Handler;
Stormy, husky, brawling,
City of the Big Shoulders:

They tell me you are wicked and I believe
    them, for I have seen your painted
    women under the gas lamps luring the
    farm boys.
And they tell me you are crooked and I
    answer: Yes, it is true I have seen
    the gunman kill and go free to kill
    again.
And they tell me you are brutal and my reply
    is: On the faces of women and children
    I have seen the marks of wanton hunger.
And having answered so I turn once more to
    those who sneer at this my city, and I
    give them back the sneer and say to them:
Come and show me another city with lifted head
    singing so proud to be alive and coarse
    and strong and cunning.
Flinging magnetic curses amid the toil of
    piling job on job, here is a tall bold
    slugger set vivid against the little
    soft cities;
Fierce as a dog with tongue lapping for
    action, cunning as a savage pitted against
    the wilderness,
        Bareheaded,
        Shoveling,
        Wrecking,
        Planning,
        Building, breaking, rebuilding.

Ken Kraska, J.S. Morton High School East, Cicero, Ill.

Under the smoke, dust all over his mouth,
    laughing with white teeth,
Under the terrible burden of destiny laughing
    as a young man laughs,
Laughing even as an ignorant fighter laughs
    who has never lost a battle,
Bragging and laughing that under his wrist is
    the pulse, and under his ribs the heart
    of the people,
      Laughing!
Laughing the stormy, husky, brawling laughter
    of Youth, half-naked, sweating, proud to
    be Hog Butcher, Tool Maker, Stacker of
    Wheat, Player with Railroads and
    Freight Handler to the Nation.

Carl Sandburg

MEETING-HOUSE HILL

I must be mad, or very tired,
When the curve of a blue bay beyond a rail-
    road track
Is shrill and sweet to me like the sudden
    springing of a tune,
And the sight of a white church above thin
    trees in a city square
Amazes my eyes as though it were the
Parthenon.
Clear, reticent, superbly final,
With the pillars of its portico refined to
    a cautious elegance,
It dominates the weak trees,
And the shot of its spire
Is cool, and candid,
Rising into an unresisting sky.
Strange meeting-house
Pausing a moment upon a squalid hilltop.
I watch the spire sweeping the sky,
I am dizzy with the movement of the sky,
I might be watching a mast
With its royals set full
Straining before a two-reef breeze.
I might be sighting a tea-clipper,
Tacking into the blue bay,
Just back from Canton
With her hold full of green and blue porcelain,
And a Chinese coolie leaning over the rail
Gazing at the white spire
With dull, sea-spent eyes.

Amy Lowell

Nadia Walter, London Central Secondary School, London, 14, Ontario

BUILDING THE FIRE
from *Snowbound*

As night drew on, and, from the crest
Of wooded knolls that ridged the west,
The sun, a snow-blown traveller, sank
From sight beneath the smothering bank,
We piled with care our nightly stack
Of wood against the chimney-back —
The oaken log, green, huge, and thick,
And on its top the stout back-stick;
The knotty forestick laid apart,
And filled between with curious art
The ragged brush; then, hovering near,
We watched the first red blaze appear,
Heard the sharp crackle, caught the gleam
On whitewashed wall and sagging beam,
Until the old, rude-furnished room
Burst, flowerlike, into rosy bloom;
While radiant with a mimic flame
Outside the sparkling drift became,
And through the bare-boughed lilac-tree
Our own warm hearth seemed blazing free.
The crane and pendent trammels showed,
The Turks' heads on the andirons glowed;
While childish fancy, prompt to tell
The meaning of the miracle,
Whispered the old rhyme: "*Under the tree
When fire outdoors burns merrily,
There the witches are making tea.*"
The moon above the eastern wood
Shone at its full; the hill-range stood
Transfigured in the silver flood,

Its blown snows flashing cold and keen,
Dead white, save where some sharp ravine
Took shadow, or the sombre green
Of hemlocks turned to pitchy black
Against the whiteness of their back.
For such a world and such a night
Most fitting that unwarming light,
Which only seemed where'er it fell
To make the coldness visible.

Shut in from all the world without,
We sat the clean-winged hearth about,
Content to let the north-wind roar
In baffled rage at pane and door,
While the red logs before us beat
The frost-line back with tropic heat;
And ever, when a louder blast
Shook beam and rafter as it passed,
The merrier up its roaring draught
The great throat of the chimney laughed,
The house dog on his paws outspread
Laid to the fire his drowsy head,
The cat's dark silhouette on the wall
A couchant tiger's seemed to fall;
And for the winter fireside meet,
Between the andirons' straddling feet,
The mug of cider simmered slow,
The apples sputtered in a row,
And close at hand, the basket stood
With nuts from brown October's wood.

John Greenleaf Whittier

I HEAR AMERICA SINGING

I hear America singing, the varied carols
  I hear,
Those of mechanics, each one singing his as it
  should be, blithe and strong,
The carpenter singing his as he measures his
  plank or beam,
The mason singing as he makes ready for work,
  or leaves off work,
The boatman singing what belongs to him in
  the boat, the deckhand singing on the
  steamboat deck,
The shoemaker singing as he sits on his bench,
  the hatter singing as he stands,
The woodcutter's song, the ploughboy's on
  his way in the morning, or at noon inter-
  mission, or at sundown,
The delicious singing of the mother, or of
  the young wife at work, or of the girl
  singing or washing,
Each singing what belongs to him or her
  and to none else,
The day that belongs to the day — at night
  the party of young fellows, robust, friendly,
Singing with open mouths their strong melodi-
  ous songs.

Walt Whitman

THE SHIP-BUILDERS

The sky is ruddy in the east,
    The earth is gray below,
And spectral in the river-mist,
    The ship's white timbers show.
Then let the sounds of measured stroke
    And grating saw begin;
The broad axe to the gnarlèd oak,
    The mallet to the pin!

Hark! roars the bellows, blast on blast,
    The sooty smithy jars,
The fire-sparks, rising far and fast,
    Are fading with the stars.
All day for us the smith shall stand
    Beside that flashing forge;
All day for us his heavy hand
    The groaning anvil scourge.

From far-off hills, the panting team
    For us is toiling near;
For us the raftsmen down the stream
    Their island barges steer.
Rings out for us the axe-man's stroke
    In forests old and still;
For us the century-circled oak
    Falls crashing down his bill.

Up! up! in nobler toil than ours
    No craftsmen bear a part:
We make of Nature's giant powers
    The slaves of human Art.
Lay rib to rib and beam to beam,

And drive the treenails free;
Nor faithless joint nor yawning seam
　　Shall tempt the searching sea!

Where'er the keel of our good ship
　　The sea's rough field shall plough:
Where'er her tossing spars shall drip
　　With salt-spray caught below;
That ship must heed her master's beck
　　Her helm obey his hand,
And seamen tread her reeling deck
　　As if they trod the land.

Her oaken ribs the vulture-beak
　　Of Northern ice may peel;
The sunken rock and coral peak
　　May grate along her keel;
And know we well the painted shell
　　We give to wind and wave,
Must float, the sailor's citadel,
　　Or sink, the sailor's grave!

Ho! strike away the bars and blocks,
　　And set the good ship free!
Why lingers on these dusty rocks
　　The young bride of the sea?
Look! how she moves adown the grooves,
　　In graceful beauty now!
How lowly on the breast she loves
　　Slinks down her virgin prow!

God bless her! Wheresoe'er the breeze
　　Her snowy wing shall fan,
Aside the frozen Hebrides
　　Or sultry Hindustan!

Where'er, in mart or on the main,
  With peaceful flag unfurled,
She helps to wind the silken chain
  Of commerce round the world!

Speed on the ship! But let her bear
  No merchandise of sin,
No groaning cargo of despair
  Her roomy hold within;
No Lethean drug for Eastern lands,
  Nor poison-draught for ours;
But honest fruits of toiling hands
  And Nature's sun and showers.

Be hers the Prairie's golden grain,
  The Desert's golden sand,
The clustered fruits of sunny Spain,
  The spice of Morning-land!
Her pathway on the open main
  May blessings follow free,
And glad hearts welcome back again
  Her white sails from the sea!

                    John Greenleaf Whittier

THE BISHOP OF ATLANTA:
RAY CHARLES

The Bishop seduces the world with his voice
Sweat strangles mute eyes
As insinuations gush out through a hydrant on
   sorrow
Dreams, a world never seen
Moulded on Africa's anvil, tempered down
   home
Documented in cries and wails
Screaming to be ignored, crooning to be
   heard
Throbbing from the gutter
On Saturday night
Silver offering only
The Right Reverend's back in town
Don't it make you feel all right?

Julian Bond

KANSAS

Oh, I have walked in Kansas
Through many a harvest field,
And piled the sheaves of glory there
And down the wild rows reeled:

Each sheaf a little yellow sun,
A heap of hot-rayed gold;
Each binder like Creation's hand
To mold suns, as of old.

Straight overhead the orb of noon
Beat down with brimstone breath:
The desert wind from south and west
Was blistering flame and death.

Yet it was gay in Kansas,
A-fighting that strong sun;
And I and many a fellow-tramp
Defied that wind and won.

And we felt free in Kansas
From any sort of fear,
For thirty thousand tramps like us
There harvest every year.

She stretches arms for them to come,
She roars for helpers then,
And so it is in Kansas
That tramps, one month, are men.

We sang in burning Kansas
The songs of Sabbath-school,
The "Day-Star" flashing in the East,
The "Vale of Eden" cool.

We sang in splendid Kansas
"The flag that set us free" —
That march of fifty thousand men
With Sherman to the sea.

We feasted high in Kansas
And had much milk and meat.
The tables groaned to give us power
Wherewith to save the wheat.

Our beds were sweet alfalfa hay
Within the barn loft wide.
The loft doors opened out upon
The endless wheat-field tide.

I loved to watch the windmills spin
And watch that big moon rise.
I dreamed and dreamed with lids half-shut,
The moonlight in my eyes.

For all men dream in Kansas
By noonday and by night,
By sunrise yellow, red and wild
And moonrise wild and white.

The wind would drive the flittering clouds,
The cottonwoods would croon,
And past the sheaves and through the leaves
Came whispers from the moon.

Vachel Lindsay

Michael Hansen, Washington Island High School, Washington Island, Wisconsin

DRIVING TOWARD THE LAC QUI PARLE RIVER

I

I am driving; it is dusk; Minnesota.
The stubble field catches the last growth of sun.
The soybeans are breathing on all sides.
Old men are sitting before their houses on carseats
In the small towns. I am happy,
The moon rising above the turkey sheds.

II

The small world of the car
Plunges through the deep fields of the night,
On the road from Willmar to Milan.
This solitude covered with iron
Moves through the fields of night
Penetrated by the noise of crickets.

III

Nearly to Milan, suddenly a small bridge,
And water kneeling in the moonlight.
In small towns the houses are built right on the ground;
The lamplight falls on all fours in the grass.
When I reach the river, the full moon falls on it;
A few people are talking low in a boat.

Robert Bly

CONCORD HYMN

By the rude bridge that arched the flood,
  Their flag to April's breeze unfurled,
Here once the embattled farmers stood
  And fired the shot heard round the world.

The foe long since in silence slept;
  Alike the conqueror silent sleeps;
And Time the ruined bridge has swept
  Down the dark stream which seaward creeps.

On this green bank, by this soft stream,
  We set today a votive stone;
That memory may their deed redeem,
  When, like our sires, our sons are gone.

Spirit, that made those heroes dare
  To die, and leave their children free,
Bid Time and Nature gently spare
  The shaft we raise to them and thee.

Ralph Waldo Emerson

Ian Klingbail, Lyndon H. Strong Junior High School, Rome, New York

PAUL REVERE'S RIDE

Listen, my children, and you shall hear
Of the midnight ride of Paul Revere,
On the eighteenth of April, in Seventy-five;
Hardly a man is now alive
Who remembers that famous day and year.

He said to his friend, "If the British march
By land or sea from the town tonight,
Hang a lantern aloft in the belfry arch
Of the North Church tower as a signal light —
One, if by land, and two, if by sea;
And I on the opposite shore will be,
Ready to ride and spread the alarm
Through every Middlesex village and farm,
For the country-folk to be up and to arm."

Then he said, "Good night!" and with muffled oar
Silently rowed to the Charlestown shore,
Just as the moon rose over the bay,
Where swinging wide at her moorings lay
The *Somerset*, British man-of-war;
A phantom ship, with each mast and spar
Across the moon like a prison bar,
And a huge black hulk, that was magnified
By its own reflection in the tide.

Meanwhile, his friend, through alley and street
Wanders and watches with eager ears,
Till in the silence around him he hears
The muster of men at the barrack door,
The sound of arms, and the tramp of feet,
And the measured tread of the grenadiers,
Marching down to their boats on the shore.

Then he climbed the tower of the Old North Church,
By the wooden stairs, with stealthy tread,
To the belfry-chamber overhead,
And startled the pigeons from their perch
On the sombre rafters, that round him made
Masses and moving shapes of shade, —
Up the trembling ladder, steep and tall,
To the highest window in the wall,
Where he paused to listen and look down
A moment on the roofs of the town,
And the moonlight flowing over all.

Beneath, in the churchyard, lay the dead,
In their night-encampment on the hill,
Wrapped in silence so deep and still
That he could hear, like a sentinel's tread,
The watchful night-wind, as it went
Creeping along from tent to tent,
And seeming to whisper, "All is well!"
A moment only he feels the spell
Of the place and the hour, and the secret dread
Of the lonely belfry and the dead;
For suddenly all his thoughts are bent
On a shadowy something far away,
Where the river widens to meet the bay —
A line of black that bends and floats
On the rising tide, like a bridge of boats.

Meanwhile, impatient to mount and ride,
Booted and spurred, with a heavy stride
On the opposite shore walked Paul Revere.
Now he patted his horse's side.
Now gazed at the landscape far and near,
Then, impetuous, stamped the earth,
And turned and tightened his saddle-girth;
But mostly he watched with eager search
The belfry-tower of the Old North Church,
As it rose above the graves on the hill,

Lonely and spectral and sombre and still.
And lo! as he looks, on the belfry's height
A glimmer, and then a gleam of light!
He springs to the saddle, the bridle he turns,
But lingers and gazes, till full on his sight
A second lamp in the belfry burns!

A hurry of hoofs in a village street,
A shape in the moonlight, a bulk in the dark,
And beneath, from the pebbles, in passing, a spark
Struck out by a steed flying fearless and fleet;
That was all! And yet, through the gloom and the light,
The fate of a nation was riding that night;
And the spark struck out by that steed, in his flight,
Kindled the land into flame with its heat.

He has left the village and mounted the steep,
And beneath him, tranquil and broad and deep,
Is the Mystic, meeting the ocean tides;
And under the alders, that skirt its edge
Now soft on the sand, now loud on the ledge,
Is heard the tramp of his steed as he rides.

It was twelve by the village clock
When he crossed the bridge into Medford town.
He heard the crowing of the cock,
And the barking of the farmer's dog,
And felt the damp of the river fog,
That rises after the sun goes down.

It was one by the village clock,
When he galloped into Lexington.
He saw the gilded weathercock
Swim in the moonlight as he passed,
And the meeting-house windows, blank and bare,
Gaze at him with a spectral glare,
As if they already stood aghast
At the bloody work they would look upon.

It was two by the village clock
When he came to the bridge in Concord town.
He heard the bleating of the flock,
And the twitter of birds among the trees,
And felt the breath of the morning breeze
Blowing over the meadows brown.
And one was safe and asleep in his bed
Who at the bridge would be first to fall,
Who that day would be lying dead,
Pierced by a British musket-ball.

You know the rest. In the books you have read,
How the British regulars fired and fled —
How the farmers gave them ball for ball,
From behind each fence and farmyard wall,
Chasing the red-coats down the lane,
Then crossing the fields to emerge again
Under the trees at the turn of the road,
And only pausing to fire and load.

So through the night rode Paul Revere;
And so through the night went his cry of alarm
To every Middlesex village and farm —
A cry of defiance and not of fear,
A voice in the darkness, a knock at the door,
And a word that shall echo for evermore!

For, borne on the night-wind of the Past,
Through all our history, to the last,
In the hour of darkness and peril and need,
The people will waken and listen to hear
The hurrying hoof-beats of that steed,
And the midnight message of Paul Revere.

Henry Wadsworth Longfellow

FOR THE GRAVE OF DANIEL BOONE

The farther he went the farther home grew.
Kentucky became another room;
the mansion arched over the Mississippi;
flowers were spread all over the floor.
He traced ahead a deepening home,
And better, with goldenrod:

Leaving the snakeskin of place after place,
going on — after the trees
the grass, a bird flying after a song.
Rifle so level, sighting so well
his picture freezes down to now,
a story-picture for children.

They go over the velvet falls
into the tapestry of his time,
heirs to the landscape, feeling no jar:
it is like evening; they are the quail
surrounding his fire, coming in for the kill;
their little feet move sacred sand.

Children, we live in a barbwire time
but like to follow the old hands back —
the ring in the light, the knuckle, the palm,
all the way to Daniel Boone,
hunting our own kind of deepening home.
From the land that was his I heft this rock.

Here on his grave I put it down.

William Stafford

CASEY JONES

Come all you rounders if you want to hear,
The story of a brave engineer.
Casey Jones was the rounder's name,
On a big six-wheeler, boys, he made his fame.
Well, the caller called Casey 'bout half past four,
He kissed his wife at the station door.
He stepped into the cabin with the orders in his hand,
Said, "I'm gonna take my trip to the Promised Land."

   Casey Jones, stepped into the cabin,
   Casey Jones, orders in his hand.
   Casey Jones, stepped into the cabin,
   Said, "I'm gonna take my trip to the Promised Land."

He looked at the water and the water was low,
He looked at his watch, the watch was slow.
He looked at the fireman, the fireman said,
"Boy, we're gonna reach 'Frisco but we'll all be dead."

Casey pulled up that Reno Hill,
He blew at the crossing with an awful shrill.
The switchman knew by the engine's moan
That the man at the throttle was Casey Jones.
Casey got to that certain place,
Old Number Nine stared him straight in the face.
He said to the fireman, "Boy, you'd better jump,
'Cause there's two locomotives and they're bound to
    bump."

   Casey Jones, two locomotives,
   Casey Jones, and they're bound to bump.
   Casey Jones, two locomotives,
   Two locomotives and they're bound to bump.

Well, Mrs. Casey Jones she sat there on the bed,
She got the telegram that her poor husband was dead.
She said, "Go to bed children and hush your cryin',
You got another papa on the Salt Lake Line."

   Casey Jones, got another papa,
   Casey Jones, on the Salt Lake Line,
   Casey Jones, got another papa,
   "You got another papa on the Salt Lake Line."

Anonymous

OLD IRONSIDES

Ay, tear her tattered ensign down!
  Long has it waved on high,
And many an eye has danced to see
  That banner in the sky;
Beneath it rung the battle shout,
  And burst the cannon's roar;
The meteor of the ocean air
  Shall sweep the clouds no more!

Her deck, once red with heroes' blood,
  Where knelt the vanquished foe,
When winds were hurrying o'er the flood,
  And waves were white below,
No more shall feel the victor's tread,
  Or know the conquered knee;
The harpies of the shore shall pluck
  The eagle of the sea!

O better that her shattered hulk
  Should sink beneath the wave;
Her thunders shook the mighty deep,
  And there should be her grave;
Nail to the mast her holy flag,
  Set every threadbare sail,
And give her to the god of storms,
  The lightning and the gale!

Oliver Wendell Holmes

GRASS

Pile the bodies high at Austerlitz and
  Waterloo.
Shovel them under and let me work —
                  I am the grass; I cover all.

And pile them high at Gettysburg
And pile them high at Ypres and Verdun.
Shovel them under and let me work.
Two years, ten years, and passengers ask the
  conductor:

  What place is this?
  Where are we now?

  I am the grass.
  Let me work.

Carl Sandburg

O CAPTAIN! MY CAPTAIN!

O Captain! my Captain! our fearful trip is done,
The ship has weather'd every rack, the prize
   we sought is won,
The port is near, the bells I hear, the people
   all exulting,
While follow eyes the steady keel, the vessel
   grim and daring;
     But O heart! heart! heart!
      O the bleeding drops of red,
       Where on the deck my Captain lies,
       Fallen cold and dead.

O Captain! my Captain! rise up and hear the bells;
Rise up — for you the flag is flung — for you
   the bugle trills,
For you bouquets and ribbon'd wreaths — for you
   the shores acrowding,
For you they call, the swaying mass, their eager
   faces turning;
     Here Captain! dear father!
      This arm beneath your head!
       It is some dream that on the deck,
       You've fallen cold and dead.

My Captain does not answer, his lips are pale and
   still,
My father does not feel my arm, he has no pulse
   nor will,
The ship is anchor'd safe and sound, its voyage
   closed and done,
From fearful trip the victor ship comes in with
   object won;

Exult O shores, and ring O bells!
  but I with mournful tread,
    Walk the deck my Captain lies,
      Fallen cold and dead.

Walt Whitman

DOWN IN DALLAS

Down in Dallas, down in Dallas,
Where the shadow of blood lies black,
Little Oswald nailed Jack Kennedy up
With the nail of a rifle crack.

The big bright Cadillacs stomped on their brakes,
The street fell unearthly still
While, smoke on its chin, that slithering gun
Coiled back from its window sill.

In a white chrome room on a table top
They tried all a scalpel knows,
But they couldn't spell stop to that drop-by-drop
Till it bloomed to a rigid rose.

Out on the altar, out on the altar,
Christ blossoms in bread and wine,
But each asphalt stone where his blood dropped down
Is burst to a cactus spine.

Oh down in Dallas, down in Dallas,
Where a desert wind walks by night,
He stood and they nailed him foot and hand
To the cross of a rifle sight.

X. J. Kennedy

ELEGY FOR J.F.K.

Why *then*? Why *there*?
Why *thus*, we cry, did he die?
The Heavens are silent.

What he was, he was:
What he is fated to become
Depends on us.

Remembering his death,
How we choose to live
Will decide its meaning.

When a just man dies,
Lamentation and praise,
Sorrow and joy are one.

W. H. Auden

GRANITE AND STEEL

(Brooklyn Bridge)

Enfranchising cable, silvered by the sea,
   of woven wire, grayed by the mist,
   and Liberty dominate the Bay —
   her feet as one on shattered chains,
   once whole links wrought by Tyranny.

   Caged Circe of steel and stone,
   her parent German ingenuity.
   "O catenary curve" from tower to pier,
   implacable enemy of the mind's deformity,
   of man's uncompunctious greed,
   his crass love of crass priority,
      just recently
   obstructing acquiescent feet
   about to step ashore when darkness fell
      without a cause,
   as if probity had not joined our cities
      in the sea.

   "O path amid the stars
   crossed by the seagull's wing!"
   "O radiance that doth inherit me!"
   — affirming interacting harmony!

   Untried expedient, untried; then tried;
   sublime elliptic two-fold egg —
   way out; way in; romantic passageway
   first seen by the eye of the mind,
   then by the eye. O steel! O stone!
   Climactic ornament, double rainbow,
   as if inverted by French perspicacity,
      John Roebling's monument,
      German tenacity's also;
      composite span — an actuality.

Marianne Moore

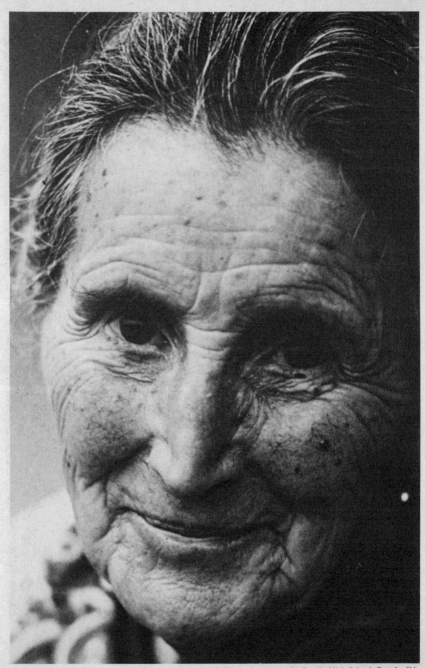

Larry Daniels, Reseda High School, Reseda, CA

IV
The First Americans

INDIANS ON THE MAINE COAST

I loved the Indian, when he built his wigwam by the
    pond
And hunted, unmolested. No canvas wigwam had he,
But one of boughs. I've sat and watched the squaws
Doing their beadwork, and wished I were an Indian.

They were our friends, and we were theirs;
They came and we welcomed them: they lived upon
    our land,
No rent was paid or asked, our children played with
    theirs.

They often made us visits, wearing their bright plaid
    shawls
And shining beaver hats. They sat at table with them
    on;
It was their custom. We treated them like honored
    guests,
And they looked it. Why should we not?
Were they not here before us?

Adelma Joy

THE INDIAN BURYING GROUND

In spite of all the learned have said,
   I still my old opinion keep;
The posture that we give the dead,
   Points out the soul's eternal sleep.

Not so the ancients of these lands —
   The Indian when from life released,
Again is seated with his friends,
   And shares again the joyous feast.

His imaged birds, and painted bowl,
   And venison, for a journey dressed,
Bespeak the nature of the soul,
   Activity, that knows no rest.

His bow, for action ready bent,
   And arrows, with a head of stone,
Can only mean that life is spent,
   And not the old ideas gone.

Thou, stranger, that shalt come this way,
   No fraud upon the dead commit —
Observe the swelling turf, and say
   They do not lie, but here they sit.

Here still a lofty rock remains,
    On which the curious eye may trace
(Now wasted, half by wearing rains)
    The fancies of a ruder race.

Here still an aged elm aspires,
    Beneath whose far-projecting shade
(And which the shepherd still admires)
    The children of the forest played!

There oft a restless Indian queen
    (Pale Shebah, with her braided hair)
And many a barbarous form is seen
    To chide the man that lingers there.

By midnight moons, o'er moistening dews;
    In habit for the chase arrayed,
The hunter still the deer pursues,
    The hunter and the deer, a shade!

And long shall timorous fancy see
    The painted chief, and pointed spear,
And Reason's self shall bow the knee
    To shadows and delusions here.

Philip Freneau

HIAWATHA'S WEDDING FEAST

You shall hear how Pau-Puk-Keewis,
How the handsome Yenadizze
Danced at Hiawatha's wedding;
How the gentle Chibiabos,
He the sweetest of musicians,
Sang his songs of love and longing;
How Iagoo, the great boaster,
He the marvellous storyteller,
Told his tales of strange adventure,
That the feast might be more joyous,
That the time might pass more gaily,
And the guests be more contented.

Sumptuous was the feast Nokomis
Made at Hiawatha's wedding;
All the bowls were made of bass-wood,
White and polished very smoothly,
All the spoons of horn of bison,
Black and polished very smoothly.

She had sent through all the village
Messengers with wands of willow,
As a sign of invitation,
As a token of the feasting;
And the wedding guests assembled,
Clad in all their richest raiment,
Robes of fur and belts of wampum,
Splendid with their paint and plumage,
Beautiful with beads and tassels.

First they ate the sturgeon, Nahma,
And the pike, the Maskenozha,
Caught and cooked by old Nokomis;
Then on pemican they feasted,
Pemican and buffalo marrow,
Haunch of deer and hump of bison,
Yellow cakes of the Mondamin,

And the wild rice of the river.
　But the gracious Hiawatha,
And the lovely Laughing Water,
And the careful old Nokomis,
Tasted not the food before them,
Only waited on the others,
Only served their guests in silence.
　And when all the guests had finished,
Old Nokomis, brisk and busy,
From an ample pouch of otter,
Filled the red-stone pipes for smoking
With tobacco from the Southland,
Mixed with bark of the red willow,
And with herbs and leaves of fragrance.
　Then she said, "O Pau-Puk-Keewis,
Dance for us your merry dances,
Dance the Beggar's Dance to please us,
That the feast may be more joyous,
That the time may pass more gaily,
And our guests be more contented!"
　Then the handsome Pau-Puk-Keewis,
He the idle Yenadizze,
He the merry mischiefmaker,
Whom the people called the Storm-Fool,
Rose among the guests assembled.
　Skilled was he in sports and pastimes,
In the merry dance of snow shoes,
In the play of quoits and ball play;
Skilled was he in games of hazard,
In all games of skill and hazard,
Pugasaing, the Bowl and Counters,
Kuntassoo, the Game of Plum-stones.
Though the warriors called him Faint-Heart,
Called him Coward, Shaugodaya,

Idler, gambler, Yenadizze,
Little heeded he their jesting,
Little cared he for their insults,
For the women and the maidens,
Loved the handsome Pau-Puk-Keewis.

He was dressed in shirt of doeskin,
White and soft, and fringed with ermine,
All inwrought with beads of wampum;
He was dressed in deerskin leggings,
Fringed with hedgehog quills and ermine,
And in moccasins of buck-skin,
Thick with quills and beads embroidered.
On his head were plumes of swan's down,
On his heels were tails of foxes,
In one hand a fan of feathers,
And a pipe was in the other.

Barred with streaks of red and yellow,
Streaks of blue and bright vermilion,
Shone the face of Pau-Puk-Keewis.
From his forehead fell his tresses,
Smooth, and parted like a woman's,
Shining bright with oil, and plaited,
Hung with braids of scented grasses,
As among the guests assembled,
To the sound of flutes and singing,
To the sound of drums and voices,
Rose the handsome Pau-Puk-Keewis,
And began his mystic dances.

First he danced a solemn measure,
Very slow in step and gesture,
In and out among the pine trees,
Through the shadows and the sunshine,
Treading softly like a panther.
Then more swiftly and still swifter,

Whirling, spinning round in circles,
Leaping o'er the guests assembled,
Eddying round and round the wigwam,
Till the leaves went whirling with him,
Till the dust and wind together
Swept in eddies round about him.

Then along the sandy margin
Of the lake, the Big-Sea-Water,
On he sped with frenzied gestures,
Stamped upon the sand, and tossed it
Wildly in the air around him;
Till the wind became a whirlwind,
Till the sand was blown and sifted
Like great snowdrifts o'er the landscape,
Heaping all the shores with Sand Dunes,
Sand Hills of the Nagow Wudjoo!

Thus the merry Pau-Puk-Keewis
Danced his Beggar's Dance to please them,
And, returning, sat down laughing
There among the guests assembled,
Sat and fanned himself serenely
With his fan of turkey-feathers.

Then they said to Chibiabos,
To the friend of Hiawatha,
To the sweetest of all singers,
To the best of all musicians,
"Sing to us, O Chibiabos!
Songs of love and songs of longing."
Looking still at Hiawatha,
Looking at fair Laughing Water,
Sang he softly, sang in this wise:

"Onaway! Awake, beloved!
Thou the wildflower of the forest!
Thou the wild bird of the prairie!

Thou with eyes so soft and fawnlike!
   "If thou only lookest at me,
I am happy, I am happy,
As the lilies of the prairie,
When they feel the dew upon them!"
   Thus the gentle Chibiabos
Sang his song of love and longing;
And Iagoo, the great boaster,
He the marvelous storyteller,
He the friend of old Nokomis,
Jealous of the sweet musician,
Jealous of the applause they gave him,
Saw in all the eyes around him,
Saw in all their looks and gestures,
That the wedding guests assembled
Longed to hear his pleasant stories,
His immeasurable falsehoods.

   Very boastful was Iagoo;
Never heard he an adventure
But himself had met a greater;
Never any deed of daring
But himself had done a bolder;
Never any marvelous story
But himself could tell a stranger.

   Would you listen to his boasting,
Would you only give him credence,
No one ever shot an arrow
Half so far and high as he had;
Ever caught so many fishes,
Ever killed so many reindeer,
Ever trapped so many reindeer,
Ever trapped so many beaver!
   None could run so fast as he could,
None could dive so deep as he could,

None could swim so far as he could;
None had made so many journeys,
None had seen so many wonders,
As this wonderful Iagoo,
As this marvelous storyteller!

   Thus his name became a by-word
And a jest among the people;
And whene'er a boastful hunter
Praised his own address too highly,
Or a warrior, home returning,
Talked too much of his achievements,
All his hearers cried, "Iagoo!
Here's Iagoo come among us!"

   He it was who carved the cradle
Of the little Hiawatha,
Carved its framework out of linden,
Bound it strong with reindeer sinews
He it was who taught him later
How to make his bows and arrows,
How to make the bows of ash-tree,
And the arrows of the oak-tree.
So among the guests assembled
At my Hiawatha's wedding
Sat Iagoo, old and ugly,
Sat the marvelous storyteller.

   And they said, "O good Iagoo,
Tell us now a tale of wonder,
Tell us of some strange adventure,
That the feast may be more joyous,
That the time may pass more gaily,
And our guests be more contented!"

Henry Wadsworth Longfellow

A MISSOURI TRAVELLER WRITES
HOME: 1830

The spring rides down; from Judith and the Larb,
Straining and full, the choked Missouri, choked
With sticks and roots, and high with floating trees
Rides down, as my mind at this oakwood table.
For May unlocks the Crazy Hills,
Pouring, as she has done before, the shattered snowfields
    down
Till the rumbling brown has burned the land away
A hundred feet below the plain
With spoils of snowfields from the Crazy Hills.
Day breaks, and the Pawnees on those cliffs
Above, shouting, keep pace with us;
The warrior trains like rocks against the sky:
At dawn we see the crumbling cliffs at first,
Then horse and rider, then the Western sky;
Those ash-grey horses black against the clouds!
Tall men, high, fierce, with shoulders as if brass
They lift long warbows made by the Dakotahs,
Above their Pawnee shields of black and white;
With cries and howls, all day they shriek on cliffs.
The buffalo, drinking at the shore, in herds
Hear, and shoulders humping, the buffalo stampede
Alarmed, up porch to porch, onto the plains of dust,
And I have heard the buffalo stampede
With muffled clatter of colliding horns.
On the whole, peril hangs above this land
Like smoke that floats at dawn above dead fires.
The Sioux believe all people, scalped or choked,
Are locked out of Paradise, yet I have seen
Small Sioux women hanging from scraggly trees;
On scaffolds stretch the acres of the dead,
Corroding in their sepulchres of air; at night
With cries, the Osage from their teepee doors,

Mourn the dead, cutting their arms, and screaming;
At dawn the buzzard flocks awake on trees, dewdamp,
And stretch their black wings toward the sun to dry.
Such are the few details that I have seen.

The River splits this country, and it seems
We see the Indians always walking Western banks,
Faced toward full sun, like nephews of the sun;
And there are signs of what will come: the whites,
With steel traps hanging, swung from saddle thongs,
Or flat Virginians, behind great round wheels:
All whites believe these Rees and Sioux and Kaws
And Mandans are not men, but damned as beasts:
Are damned; are held knit in damnation now
Like grasp of snakes, in Satan's grasp himself,
And like the serpent's hold, it is by death alone
To be released: The Sioux are still and silent
Generally, and I have watched them stand
By ones and twos upon the river's bank
As glum as Hudson's blankets winding them,
While shuttling steamboats smoke, labouring up
The breaking foam, beyond the cottonwoods,
Into the region of their dead and of their youth,
Pushed up, they say, by smoke; and they believe
The tribe of whites, like smoke, soon shall return
From whence it came: and therefore in both minds
The truth is absent; and the hands alone
Are like the willow trees, forever green
And undeceived: the hands continue killing.
The hands go on, the minds remain behind,
As if the concepts handled by the mind
Were lesser than the concepts of the hands,
As if a man achieves more than he knows;

Or if the pain of action were so great
And life so freezing and Medusa-faced,
That, like Medusa's head, it could be held
And not observed, lest eye's reward be stone.

The night grows old above this river boat.
Before I end, I shall include account
Of an incident tonight that moved my wonder.
At dusk we tied the boat to trees on shore;
No mortal boat in these night shoals can live.
At first I heard a cry: shuffling and cries
And muffled sounds on deckoak overhead
Drew me on deck, the air was chill, and there
I sensed, because these senses here are sharp
And must be, something living and unknown.
To night and North a crowd stared from the boatrail,
Upriver, nightward and North: a speck of white.
The thing was white: the resonance of night
Returned its grunts and whistling on the air.
The frontier men swore in that river thicket
In ambush like the beasts they're modeled on,
Bristling for war, would be a thresh of Sioux;
The crew and gamblers nudged, to bait the settlers,
And arms nudged cry, "Along the river there's
Some settler's cow, Hereford or Poland China,
Some farmer could not nail tight enough in cribs.
And terrorizing frogs and catfish now."
But Mormons see some robe in that faint white,
In that dim white the angel of death, come
In cottonwoods to sign the Second Coming;
And on the river's border there they see
Some angel of Joseph upon the chill Missouri;
One man believed that there was nothing there,

As the moon too is false, and its white is false.
I sensed a fear, as if the wind protected it.
When the talk died, eight men, and I with them,
Set off, and moving overboard in dark,
With guns, protected by the thunder's noise,
Up the dark river, toward where the splashes rose,
So armed in case of Sioux, to our surprise
We found a white and wounded Northern Bear,
Shot in that day about the snout and head.
The pure-white bear, not native to these parts,
But to the Horns, or Ranges born, and shot
That morning, had turned downward South and East,
And had apparently through these dry plains
Passed South, to lay its burning paws and head
And lay its fever-proud and festered flesh
Within the cool Missouri's turbid bed.
Soon after, clouds of rain drove us indoors,
And lightning fell like sheets upon the sand,
Said to be sudden in these Western lands.
Minutes before it broke, a circling mass
Of split-tail swallows came and then were gone.
But now to bed. We disembark at dawn
And start to westward through the heavy grass.

Robert Bly

VACATION

One scene as I bow to pour her coffee:

Three Indians in the scouring drouth
huddle at a grave scooped in the gravel,
lean to the wind as our train goes by.
Someone is gone.
There is dust on everything in Nevada.

I pour the cream.

William Stafford

AT THE KLAMATH BERRY FESTIVAL

The war chief danced the old way —
the eagle wing he held before his mouth —
and when he turned the boom-boom
stopped. He took two steps. A sociologist
was there; the Scout troop danced.
I envied him the places where he had not been.

The boom began again. Outside he heard
the stick game, and the Blackfoot gamblers
arguing at poker under lanterns.
Still-moccasined and bashful, holding
the eagle wing before his mouth,
listening and listening, he danced after others stopped.

He took two steps, the boom caught up,
the mountains rose, the still deep river
slid, but never broke its quiet.
I looked back when I left:
he took two steps, he took two steps,
past the sociologist.

William Stafford

THE MOCCASINS OF AN OLD MAN

I hung you there, moccasins of worn buckskin.
I hung you there and there you are still.
I took you from the hot flesh of a swift buck.
I took you to my woman.

She tanned you with buck brains.
She cut and sewed and beaded.
I wore you with pride.
I wore you with leaping steps over many grounds.

Now, I sit here and my bones are stiff with many win-
    ters.
You hang there and I shall sit.
We shall watch the night approach.

Ramona Carden

GRANDFATHER

Grandfather sings, I dance.
Grandfather speaks, I listen.
Now I sing, who will dance?
I speak, who will listen?

Grandfather hunts, I learn.
Grandfather fishes, I clean.
Now I hunt, who will learn?
I fish, who will clean?

Grandfather dies, I weep.
Grandfather buried, I am left alone.
When I am dead, who will cry?
When I am buried, who will be alone?

Shirley Crawford

Eve Arnold/Magnum

UNCERTAIN ADMISSION

The sky looks down on me in aimless blues
The sun glares at me with a questioning light
The mountains tower over me with uncertain shadows
The trees sway in the bewildered breeze
The deer dance in perplexed rhythms
The ants crawl around me in untrusting circles
The birds soar above me with doubtful dips and dives
They all, in their own way, ask the question,
Who are you, who are you?
I have to admit to them, to myself,
I am an Indian.

Frances Bazil

Katie Rink, Brown County Ursulines Academy, St. Martin, Ohio

BATTLE WON IS LOST

They said, "You are no longer a lad."
     I nodded.
They said, "Enter the council lodge."
     I sat.
They said, "Our lands are at stake."
     I scowled.
They said, "We are at war."
     I hated.
They said, "Prepare red war symbols."
     I painted.
They said, "Count coups."
     I scalped.
They said, "You'll see friends die."
     I cringed.
They said, "Desperate warriors fight best."
     I charged.
They said, "Some will be wounded."
     I bled.
They said, "To die is glorious."
       They lied.

Phil George

BALLAD OF IRA HAYES

Call him drunken Ira Hayes, he won't answer any
    more;
Not the whiskey drinkin' Indian, nor the marine that
    went to war.
Gather 'round me, people, and a story I will tell
About a brave young Indian you should remember
    well,
From the tribe of Pima Indians, the proud and peaceful
    band,
Who farmed the Phoenix Valley in Arizona land.

Down their ditches for a thousand years that sparklin'
    water rushed
Till the white man stole the water rights and the run-
    nin' water hushed.
Now Ira's folks were hungry and their farm grew
    crops of weeds.
When war came Ira volunteered and forgot the white
    man's greed.

Call him drunken Ira Hayes, he won't answer any more;
Not the whiskey drinkin' Indian, nor the marine that
    went to war.

Well, they started up Iwo Jima Hill — two hundred
    and fifty men,
But only twenty-seven lived — to walk back down
    again;
And when that fight was over — and Old Glory raised,
Among the men who held it high was the Indian — Ira
    Hayes.

Call him drunken Ira Hayes, he won't answer any
    more;

Not the whiskey drinkin' Indian, nor the marine that
went to war.

Ira Hayes returned a hero — celebrated through this
land,
He was wined and speeched and honored, and everybody shook his hand;
But he was just a Pima Indian — no water, no crops, no
chance;
At home nobody cared what Ira done — and when do
the Indians dance?

Call him drunken Ira Hayes, he won't answer any
more;
Not the whiskey drinkin' Indian, nor the marine that
went to war.

Then Ira started drinkin' hard — jail often was his
home;
They let him raise the flag there, and lower it — as
you'd throw a dog a bone.
He died drunk early one morning — alone in this land
he'd fought to save;
Two inches of water in a lonely ditch was the grave for
Ira Hayes.

Call him drunken Ira Hayes, he won't answer any
more;
Not the whiskey drinkin' Indian, nor the marine that
went to war.

Yes, call him drunken Ira Hayes — but his lands they're
still as dry,
And his ghost is a-lyin' thirsty in the ditch where Ira
died.

Peter La Farge

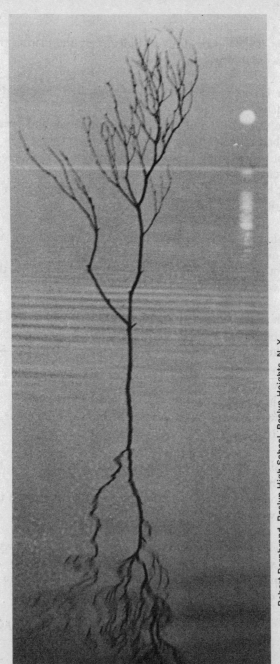

Robert Dornbrand, Roslyn High School, Roslyn Heights, N. Y.

THE SENECAS

(As Long as the Grass Shall Grow)

The Senecas are an Indian tribe,
Of the Iroquois nation,
Down on the New York-Pennsylvania line,
You'll find their reservation.
After the U.S. revolution,
Cornplanter was a chief,
He told his tribe these men they could trust
That was his true belief,
He went down to Independence Hall,
And there a treaty signed,
That promised peace with the U.S.A.,
And Indian rights combined,
George Washington gave his signature,
And the Government gave its hand,
They said that now and forever more,
This was Indian Land.

Chorus: As long as the moon shall rise,
     As long as the rivers flow,
     As long as the sun will shine
     As long as the grass shall grow.

On the Seneca reservation,
There is much sadness now,
Washington's treaty has been broken,
And there is no hope, nohow,
All across the Allegheny River,
They're throwing up a dam,
It will flood the Indian Country,
A proud day for Uncle Sam,
It has broken the ancient treaty,
With a politician's grin,

It will drown the Indians' graveyards,
Cornplanter, can you swim?
The Earth is Mother to the Senecas,
And they're trampling sacred ground,
Change the mint green earth to black mud flats,
As honor hobbles down.

Chorus: As long as the moon shall rise,
    As long as the rivers flow,
    As long as the sun will shine
    As long as the grass shall grow.

The Iroquois Indians used to rule,
From Canada way south,
But no one fears the Indians now,
And smiles the liar's mouth,
The Senecas hired an expert,
To figure another site,
But the great good army engineers,
Said that he had no right,
Although he showed them another plan,
And showed them another way,
They laughed in his face and said no deal,
Kinuza Dam is here to stay,
Congress turned the Indians down,
Brushed off the Indians' plea,
So the Senecas have renamed the dam,
They call it Lake Perfidy.

Chorus: As long as the moon shall rise,
    As long as the rivers flow,
    As long as the sun will shine
    As long as the grass shall grow.

Washington, Adams, and Kennedy,
Now hear their pledges ring,
The treaties are safe, we'll keep our word,

But what is that gurgling?
It's the backwater from Perfidy Lake
It's rising all the time,
Over the homes and over the fields,
Over the promises fine,
No boats will sail on Lake Perfidy,
And in winter it will fill,
But in summer it will be a swamp,
And all the fish will kill,
But the Government of the U.S.A.
Has corrected George's vow,
The father of our country must be wrong,
What's an Indian, anyhow.

Chorus: As long as the moon shall rise,
     As long as the rivers flow,
     As long as the sun will shine
     As long as the grass shall grow.

Peter La Farge

Jimmy Griffin, Myers Park High School, Charlotte, N.C.

V
With a Moral– Spoken or Unspoken

A CAUTION TO EVERYBODY

Consider the auk;
Becoming extinct because he forgot how to fly, and
 could only walk.
Consider man, who may well become extinct
Because he forgot how to walk and learned how to fly
 before he thinked.

Ogden Nash

MOUSE NIGHT: ONE OF OUR GAMES

We heard thunder. Nothing great — on high
ground rain began. Who ran through
that rain? I shrank, a fieldmouse, when
the thunder came — under grass with bombs
of water scything stems. My tremendous
father cowered: "Lions rushing make
that sound," he said; "we'll be brain-washed
for sure if head-size chunks of water hit us.
Duck and cover! It takes a man
to be a mouse this night," he said.

William Stafford

MOTTO

I play it cool
and dig all jive
That's the reason
I stay alive.
My motto,
As I live and learn,
  is:
Dig and Be Dug
In Return.

Langston Hughes

THE MOUNTAIN AND THE SQUIRREL

The mountain and the squirrel
Had a quarrel,
And the former called the latter "Little prig":
Bun replied,
"You are doubtless very big;
But all sorts of things and weather
Must be taken in together
To make up a year,
And a sphere.
And I think it no disgrace
To occupy my place.
If I'm not so large as you,
You are not so small as I,
And not half so spry:
I'll not deny you make
A very pretty squirrel track.
Talents differ; all is well and wisely put;
If I cannot carry forests on my back,
Neither can you crack a nut."

Ralph Waldo Emerson

Dean Rowsam, Lester B. Foreman High School, Fairport, NY

OPPORTUNITY

This I beheld, or dreamed it in a dream:
There spread a cloud of dust along a plain;
And underneath the cloud, or in it, raged
A furious battle, and men yelled, and swords
Shocked upon swords and shields. A prince's banner
Wavered, then staggered backward, hemmed by foes.
A craven hung along the battle's edge,
And thought, "Had I a sword of keener steel —
That blue blade that the king's son bears — but this
Blunt thing!" he snapped and flung it from his hand,
And lowering crept away and left the field.
Then came the king's son, wounded, sore bestead,
And weaponless, and saw the broken sword,
Hilt-buried in the dry and trodden sand,
And ran and snatched it, and with battle-shout
Lifted afresh he hewed his enemy down,
And saved a great cause that heroic day.

Edward Rowland Sill

YUSSOUF

A stranger came one night to Yussouf's tent,
Saying, "Behold one outcast and in dread,
Against whose life the bow of power is bent.
Who flies, and hath not where to lay his head;
I come to thee for shelter and for food —
To Yussouf, called through all our tribes 'The Good.' "

"This tent is mine," said Yussouf, "but no more
Than it is God's; come in, and be at peace;
Freely shalt thou partake of all my store
As I of His who buildeth over these
Our tents His glorious roof of night and day,
And at Whose door none ever yet heard 'Nay.' "

So Yussouf entertained his guest that night,
And, waking him ere day, said: "Here is gold;
My swiftest horse is saddled for thy flight;
Depart before the prying day grow bold."
As one lamp lights another, nor grows less,
So nobleness enkindleth nobleness.

That inward light the stranger's face made grand,
Which shines from all self-conquest; kneeling low,
He bowed his forehead upon Yussouf's hand,
Sobbing: "O Sheik, I cannot leave thee so;
I will repay thee; all this thou hast done
Unto that Ibrahim who slew thy son!"

"Take thrice the gold," said Yussouf, "for with thee
Into the desert, never to return,
My one black thought shall ride away from me.
First-born, for whom by day and night I yearn,
Balanced and just are all of God's decrees;
Thou art avenged, my first-born; sleep in peace!"

James Russell Lowell

THE BLIND MEN AND
THE ELEPHANT

It was six men of Indostan
   To learning much inclined,
Who went to see the Elephant
   (Though all of them were blind),
That each by observation
   Might satisfy his mind.

The *First* approached the Elephant,
   And happening to fall
Against his broad and sturdy side,
   At once began to bawl:
"God bless me! but the Elephant
   Is very like a wall!"

The *Second*, feeling of the tusk,
   Cried, "Ho! what have we here
So very round and smooth and sharp?
   To me 'tis mighty clear
This wonder of an Elephant
   Is very like a spear!"

The *Third* approached the animal,
   And happening to take
The squirming trunk within his hands,
   Thus boldly up and spake:
"I see," quoth he, "the Elephant
   Is very like a snake."

The *Fourth* reached out an eager hand,
   And felt about the knee.
"What most this wondrous beast is like

Is mighty plain," quoth he;
" 'Tis clear enough the Elephant
    Is very like a tree!"

The *Fifth,* who chanced to touch the ear,
    Said: "E'en the blindest man
Can tell what this resembles most;
    Deny the fact who can,
This marvel of an Elephant
    Is very like a fan!"

The *Sixth* no sooner had begun
    About the beast to grope,
Than, seizing on the swinging tail
    That fell within his scope,
"I see," quoth he, "the Elephant
    Is very like a rope!"

And so these men of Indostan
    Disputed loud and long,
Each in his own opinion
    Exceeding stiff and strong,
Though each was partly in the right,
    And all were in the wrong!

So oft in theologic wars,
    The disputants, I ween,
Rail on in utter ignorance
    Of what each other mean,
And prate about an Elephant
    Not one of them has seen!

                    John Godfrey Saxe

138

ONCE TO EVERY MAN AND NATION

Once to every man and nation comes the moment to
  decide,
In the strife of Truth with Falsehood, for the good or
  evil side;
Some great cause, God's new Messiah, offering each the
  bloom or blight,
And the choice goes by forever 'twixt that darkness
  and that light.

Then to side with Truth is noble, when we share her
  wretched crust,
Ere her cause bring fame and profit, and 'tis prosperous
  to be just;
Then it is the brave man chooses, while the coward
  stands aside,
Till the multitude make virtue of the faith they had
  denied.

By the light of burning heretics Christ's bleeding feet
  I track,
Toiling up new Calvaries ever with the cross that turns
  not back.
New occasions teach new duties; Time makes ancient
  good uncouth.
They must upward still, and onward, who would keep
  abreast of Truth.

Though the cause of Evil prosper, yet 'tis Truth alone
    is strong;
Though Truth's portion be the scaffold, and upon the
    throne be Wrong,
Yet that scaffold sways the future, and behind the dim
    unknown,
Standeth God within the shadow, keeping watch above
    His own.

James Russell Lowell
Adapted from *The Present Crisis*

WATCHING THE JET PLANES DIVE

We must go back and find a trail on the ground
back of the forest and mountain on the slow land;
we must begin to circle on the intricate sod.
By such wild beginnings without help we may find
the small trail on through the buffalo-bean vines.

We must go back with noses and the palms of our
    hands
and climb over the map in far places, everywhere,
and lie down whenever there is doubt and sleep there.
If roads are unconnected we must make a path,
no matter how far it is, or how lowly we arrive.

We must find something forgotten by everyone alive,
and make some fabulous gesture when the sun goes
    down
as they do by custom in little Mexico towns
where they crawl for some ritual up a rocky steep.
The jet planes dive; we must travel on our knees.

William Stafford

TO DAVID, ABOUT HIS EDUCATION

The world is full of mostly invisible things,
And there is no way but putting the mind's eye,
Or its nose, in a book, to find them out,
Things like the square root of Everest
Or how many times Byron goes into Texas,
Or whether the law of the excluded middle
Applies west of the Rockies. For these
And the like reasons, you have to go to school
And study books and listen to what you are told,
And sometimes try to remember. Though I don't know
What you will do with the mean annual rainfall
On Plato's Republic, or the calorie content
Of the Diet of Worms, such things are said to be
Good for you, and you will have to learn them
In order to become one of the grown-ups
Who sees invisible things neither steadily nor whole,
But keeps gravely the grand confusion of the world
Under his hat, which is where it belongs,
And teaches small children to do this in their turn.

Howard Nemerov

ARITHMETIC

Arithmetic is where numbers fly like pigeons
    in and out of your head.
Arithmetic tells you how many you lose or
    win if you know how many you had before
    you lost or won.
Arithmetic is seven eleven all good children
    go to heaven — or five six bundle of sticks.
Arithmetic is numbers you squeeze from your
    head to your hand to your pencil to your
    paper till you get the answer.
Arithmetic is where the answer is right
    and everything is nice and you can look
    out of the window and see the blue sky
    — or the answer is wrong and you have to
    start all over and try again and
    see how it comes out this time.
If you take a number and double it and double
    it again and then double it a few more times,
    the number gets bigger and bigger and
    goes higher and higher and only arithmetic
    can tell you what the number is when you
    decide to quit doubling.
Arithmetic is where you have to multiply —
    and you carry the multiplication table in
    your head and hope you won't lose it.
If you have two animal crackers, one good and
    one bad, and you eat one and a striped zebra
    with streaks all over him eats the other,
    how many animal crackers will you have if
    somebody offers you five six seven and you
    say No no no and you say Nay nay nay and you
    say Nix nix nix?

If you ask your mother for one fried egg for
breakfast and she gives you two fried
eggs and you eat both of them, who is
better in arithmetic, you or your mother?

Carl Sandburg

Edward Cho, South Shore High School, Chicago, ILL.

WHEN I HEARD THE LEARN'D ASTRONOMER

When I heard the learn'd astronomer,
When the proofs, the figures, were ranged in columns
    before me,
When I was shown the charts and diagrams, to add,
    divide, and measure them,
When I sitting heard the astronomer where he lectured
    with much applause in the lecture-room,
How soon unaccountable I became tired and sick,
Till rising and gliding out I wander'd off by myself,
In the mystical moist night-air, and from time to time,
Look'd up in perfect silence at the stars.

Walt Whitman

Susan Hirsch, Rincon High School, Tucson, Ariz.

TWO TRAMPS IN MUD TIME

Out of the mud two strangers came
And caught me splitting wood in the yard.
And one of them put me off my aim
By hailing cheerily "Hit them hard!"
I knew pretty well why he dropped behind
And let the other go on a way.
I knew pretty well what he had in mind:
He wanted to take my job for pay.

Good blocks of oak it was I split,
As large around as the chopping block;
And every piece I squarely hit
Fell splinterless as a cloven rock.
The blows that a life of self-control
Spares to strike for the common good
That day, giving a loose to my soul,
I spent on the unimportant wood.

The sun was warm but the wind was chill.
You know how it is with an April day
When the sun is out and the wind is still,
You're one month on in the middle of May.
But if you so much as dare to speak,
A cloud comes over the sunlit arch,
A wind comes off a frozen peak,
And you're two months back in the middle of March.

A bluebird comes tenderly up to alight
And turns to the wind to unruffle a plume
His song so pitched as not to excite
A single flower as yet to bloom.
It is snowing a flake: and he half knew
Winter was only playing possum.
Except in color he isn't blue,
But he wouldn't advise a thing to blossom.

The water for which we may have to look
In summertime with a witching-wand,
In every wheelrut's now a brook,
In every print of a hoof a pond.
Be glad of water, but don't forget
The lurking frost in the earth beneath
That will steal forth after the sun is set
And show on the water its crystal teeth.

The time when most I loved my task
These two must make me love it more
By coming with what they came to ask.
You'd think I never had felt before
The weight of an ax-head poised aloft,
The grip on earth of outspread feet.
The life of muscles rocking soft
And smooth and moist in vernal heat.

Out of the woods two hulking tramps
(From sleeping God knows where last night,
But not long since in the lumber camps).
They thought all chopping was theirs of right.
Men of the woods and lumberjacks,
They judged me by their appropriate tool.
Except as a fellow handled an ax,
They had no way of knowing a fool.

Nothing on either side was said.
They knew they had but to stay their stay
And all their logic would fill my head;
As that I had no right to play
With what was another man's work for gain.
My right might be love but theirs was need.
And where the two exist in twain
Theirs was the better right — agreed.

But yield who will to their separation,
My object in living is to unite
My avocation and my vocation
As my two eyes make one in sight.
Only where love and need are one,
And the work is play for mortal stakes,
Is the deed ever really done
For Heaven and the future's sakes.

Robert Frost

A SOLDIER

He is that fallen lance that lies as hurled,
That lies unlifted now, come dew, come rust,
But still lies pointed as it plowed the dust.
If we who sight along it round the world,
See nothing worthy to have been its mark,
It is because like men we look too near,
Forgetting that as fitted to the sphere,
Our missiles always make too short an arc.
They fall, they rip the grass, they intersect
The curve of earth, and striking, break their own;
They make us cringe for metal-point on stone.
But this we know, the obstacle that checked
And tripped the body, shot the spirit on
Further than target ever showed or shone.

Robert Frost

Harvey Stein

VI
The Play of Words

THE PURIST

I give you now Professor Twist
A conscientious scientist.
Trustees exclaimed, "He never bungles!"
And sent him off to distant jungles.
Camped on a tropic riverside,
One day he missed his loving bride.
She had, the guide informed him later,
Been eaten by an alligator.
Professor Twist could not but smile.
"You mean," he said, "a crocodile."

Ogden Nash

ELETELEPHONY

Once there was an elephant,
Who tried to use the telephant —
No! no! I mean an elephone
Who tried to use the telephone —
(Dear me! I am not certain quite
That even now I've got it right.)
Howe'er it was, he got his trunk
Entangled in the telephunk;
The more he tried to get it free,
The louder buzzed the telephee —
(I fear I'd better drop the song
Of elephop and telephong!)

Laura Richards

156

THE MODERN HIAWATHA

When he killed the Mudjokivis,
Of the skin he made him mittens,
Made them with the fur side inside,
Made them with the skin side outside,
He, to get the warm side inside,
Put the inside skin side outside;
He, to get the cold side outside,
Put the warm side fur side inside.
That's why he put the fur side inside,
Why he put the skin side outside,
Why he turned them inside outside.

George A. Strong

COMING AND GOING

The crows are cawing,
The cocks are crowing,
The roads are thawing,
The boys are thumbing,
The winds are blowing,
The year is coming.

The jays are jawing,
The cows are lowing,
The trees are turning,
The saws are sawing,
The fires are burning,
The year is going.

Robert Francis

LAMA

The one-l lama,
He's a priest.
The two-l llama,
He's a beast.

And I will bet
A silk pajama
There' isn't any
Three-l lllama.

Ogden Nash

COUNTING-OUT RHYME

Silver bark of beech, and sallow
Bark of yellow birch and yellow
  Twig of willow.

Stripe of green in moosewood maple,
Colour seen in leaf of apple,
  Bark of popple.

Wood of popple pale as moonbeam,
Wood of oak of yoke and barn-beam,
  Wood of hornbeam.

Silver bark of beech, and hollow
Stem of elder, tall and yellow
  Twig of willow.

Edna St. Vincent Millay

Dennis Pierce, Santa Monica (Calif.)
High School

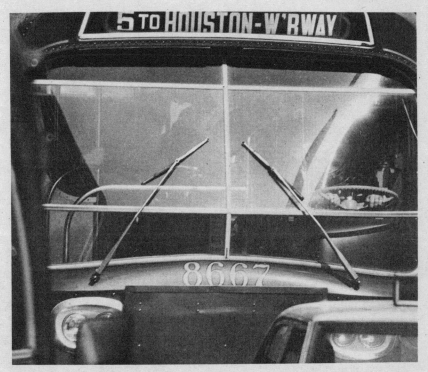

Roger Malloch/Magnum

CAPACITY

Capacity 26 Passengers
—*sign in a bus*

Affable, bibulous,
corpulent, dull,
eager-to-find-a-seat,
formidable,
garrulous, humorous,
icy, jejune,
knockabout, laden-
with-luggage (maroon),
mild-mannered, narrow-necked,
oval-eyed, pert,
querulous, rakish,
seductive, tart, vert-
iginous, willowy,
xanthic (or yellow),
young, zebuesque are my
passengers fellow.

John Updike

PHIZZOG

This face you got,
This here phizzog you carry around,
You never picked it out for yourself,
    at all, at all — did you?
This here phizzog — somebody handed it
    to you — am I right?
Somebody said, "Here's yours, now go see
    what you can do with it."
Somebody slipped it to you and it was
    like a package marked:
"No goods exchanged after being taken
    away" —
This face you got.

Carl Sandburg

NOT JUST FOR THE RIDE

There was a young lady of Niger
Who went for a ride on a tiger:
    They came back from the ride
    With the lady inside
And a smile on the face of the tiger.

Anonymous

EDOUARD

A bugler named Dougal MacDougal
Found ingenious ways to be frugal.
   He learned how to sneeze
   In various keys,
Thus saving the price of a bugle.

Ogden Nash

REQUIEM

There was a young belle of old Natchez
Whose garments were always in patchez.
   When comments arose
   On the state of her clothes,
She drawled, "When Ah itchez, Ah scratchez.

Ogden Nash

VELVET SHOES

Let us walk in the white snow
  In a soundless space;
With footsteps quiet and slow,
  At a tranquil pace,
  Under veils of white lace.

I shall go shod in silk,
  And you in wool,
White as a white cow's milk
  More beautiful
  Than the breast of a gull.

We shall walk through the still town
  In a windless peace;
We shall step upon white down,
  Upon silver fleece,
  Upon softer than these.

We shall walk in velvet shoes:
  Wherever we go
Silence will fall like dews
  On white silence below.
  We shall walk in the snow.

Elinor Wylie

Kathy Richardson, Herbert Hoover High School, Glendale, CA

DEPARTMENTAL

An ant on the tablecloth
Ran into a dormant moth
Of many times his size.
He showed not the least surprise.
His business wasn't with such.
He gave it scarcely a touch,
And was off on his duty run.
Yet if he encountered one
Of the hive's enquiry squad
Whose work is to find out God
And the nature of time and space,
He would put him onto the case.
Ants are a curious race;
One crossing with hurried tread
The body of one of their dead
Isn't given a moment's arrest —
Seems not even impressed.
But he no doubt reports to any
With whom he crosses antennae,
And they no doubt report
To the higher up at court.
Then word goes forth in Formic:

"Death's come to Jerry McCormic,
Our selfless forager Jerry.
Will the special Janizary
Whose office it is to bury
The dead of the commissary
Go bring him home to his people.
Lay him in state on a sepal.
Wrap him for shroud in a petal
Embalm him with ichor of nettle.
This is the word of your Queen."
And presently on the scene
Appears a solemn mortician;
And taking formal position
With feelers calmly atwiddle,
Seizes the dead by the middle,
And heaving him high in air,
Carries him out of there.
No one stands round to stare.
It is nobody else's affair.

It couldn't be called ungentle.
But how thoroughly departmental.

Robert Frost

Stephen Douthat, Campbell County High School, Alexandria, Kentucky

ARCHY AND MEHITABEL

i

the coming of archy

The circumstances of Archy's first appearance are narrated in the following extract from the Sun Dial column of the New York *Sun*.

Dobbs Ferry possesses a rat which slips out of his lair at night and runs a typewriting machine in a garage. Unfortunately, he has always been interrupted by the watchman before he could produce a complete story.

It was at first thought that the power which made the typewriter run was a ghost, instead of a rat. It seems likely to us that it was both a ghost and a rat. Mme. Blavatsky's ego went into a white horse after she passed over, and someone's personality has undoubtedly gone into this rat. It is an era of belief in communications from the spirit land.

And since this matter had been reported in the public prints and seriously received we are no longer afraid of being ridiculed, and we do not mind making a statement of something that happened to our own typewriter only a couple of weeks ago.

We came into our room earlier than usual in the morning, and discovered a gigantic cockroach jumping about upon the keys.

He did not see us, and we watched him. He would climb painfully upon the framework of the machine and cast himself with all his force upon a key, head downward, and his weight and the impact of the blow were just sufficient to operate the machine, one slow letter after another. He could not work the capital letters, and he had a great deal of difficulty operating the mechanism that shifts the paper so that a fresh line may be started. We never saw a cockroach work so hard or perspire so freely in all our lives before. After about an hour of this frightfully difficult literary labor he fell to the floor exhausted, and we saw him creep feebly into a nest of the poems which are always there in profusion.

Congratulating ourself that we had left a sheet of paper in the machine the night before so that all this work had not been in vain, we made an examination, and this is what we found:

expression is the need of my soul
i was once a vers libre bard
but i died and my soul went into the body of a cock-
    roach
it has given me a new outlook upon life

i see things from the under side now
thank you for the apple peelings in the wastepaper
    basket
but your paste is getting so stale i cant eat it
there is a cat here called mehitabel i wish you would
    have
removed she nearly ate me the other night why dont
    she
catch rats that is what she is supposed to be for
there is a rat here she should get without delay

most of these rats here are just rats
but this rat is like me he has a human soul in him
he used to be a poet himself
night after night i have written poetry for you
on your typewriter
and this big brute of a rat who used to be a poet
comes out of his hole when it is done
and reads it and sniffs at it
he is jealous of my poetry
he used to make fun of it when we were both human
he was a punk poet himself
and after he has read it he sneers
and then he eats it

i wish you would have mehitabel kill that rat
or get a cat that is onto her job
and i will write you a series of poems showing how
    things look
to a cockroach
that rats name is freddy
the next time freddy dies i hope he wont be a rat
but something smaller i hope i will be a rat
in the next transmigration and freddy a cockroach
i will teach him to sneer at my poetry then

dont you ever eat any sandwiches in your office
i havent had a crumb of bread for i dont know how
    long
or a piece of ham or anything but apple parings
and paste leave a piece of paper in your machine
every night you can call me archy

Don Marquis

ii
mehitabel was once cleopatra

boss i am disappointed in
some of your readers they
are always asking how does
archy work the shift so as to get a
new line or how does archy do
this or do that they
are always interested in technical
details when the main question is
whether the stuff is
literature or not
i wish you would leave
that book of george moores on
the floor
mehitabel the cat and i want to
read it i have discovered that
mehitabels soul formerly inhabited a
human also at least that
is what mehitabel is claiming these
days it may be she got jealous of
my prestige anyhow she and
i have been talking it over in a
friendly way who were you
mehitabel i asked her i was
cleopatra once she said well i said i
suppose you lived in a palace you bet
she said and what lovely fish dinners
we used to have and licked her chops
mehitabel would sell her soul for
a plate of fish any day i told her i thought
you were going to say you were
the favorite wife of the emperor
valerian he was some cat nip eh
mehitabel but she did not get me

archy

iii
the lesson of the moth

i was talking to a moth
the other evening
he was trying to break into
an electric light bulb
and fry himself on the wires

why do you fellows
pull this stunt i asked him
because it is the conventional
thing for moths or why
if that had been an uncovered
candle instead of an electric
light bulb you would
now be a small unsightly cinder
have you no sense

plenty of it he answered
but at times we get tired
of using it
we get bored with the routine
and crave beauty
and excitement

fire is beautiful
and we know that if we get
too close it will kill us
but what does that matter
it is better to be happy
for a moment
and be burned up with beauty
than to live a long time
and be bored all the while
so we wad all our life up

into one little roll
and then we shoot the roll
that is what life is for
it is better to be a part of beauty
for one instant and then cease to
exist than to exist forever
and never be a part of beauty
our attitude toward life
is come easy go easy
we are like human beings
used to be before they became
too civilized to enjoy themselves

and before i could argue him
out of his philosophy
he went and immolated himself
on a patent cigar lighter
i do not agree with him
myself i would rather have
half the happiness and twice
the longevity

but at the same time i wish
there was something i wanted
as badly as he wanted to fry himself

archy

iv
the hen and the oriole

well boss did it
ever strike you that a
hen regrets it just as
much when they wring her

174

neck as an oriole but
nobody has any
sympathy for a hen because
she is not beautiful
while everyone gets
sentimental over the
oriole and says how
shocking to kill the
lovely thing this thought
comes to my mind
because of the earnest
endeavor of a
gentleman to squash me
yesterday afternoon when i
was riding up in the
elevator if i had been a
butterfly he would have
said how did that
beautiful thing happen to
find its way into
these grimy city streets do
not harm the splendid
creature but let it
fly back to its rural
haunts again beauty always
gets the best of
it be beautiful boss
a thing of beauty is a
joy forever
be handsome boss and let
who will be clever is
the sad advice
of your ugly little friend

archy

Don Marquis

THE RAVEN

Once upon a midnight dreary, while I pondered, weak
    and weary,
Over many a quaint and curious volume of forgotten
    lore,
While I nodded, nearly napping, suddenly there came a
    tapping,
As of some one gently rapping, rapping at my chamber
    door.
" 'Tis some visitor," I muttered, "tapping at my cham-
    ber door—
      Only this and nothing more."

Ah, distinctly I remember it was in the bleak Decem-
    ber,
And each separate dying ember wrought its ghost upon
    the floor.
Eagerly I wished the morrow; vainly I had sought to
    borrow
From my books surcease of sorrow — sorrow for the
    lost Lenore,
For the rare and radiant maiden whom the angels name
    Lenore —
      Nameless *here* for evermore.

And the silken, sad, uncertain rustling of each purple
    curtain
Thrilled me — filled me with fantastic terrors never
    felt before;
So that now, to still the beating of my heart, I stood
    repeating,
" 'Tis some visitor entreating entrance at my chamber
    door —
Some late visitor entreating entrance at my chamber
    door —
      This it is and nothing more."

Gary Shonyo, Campbell High School, Ewa Beach, Hawaii

Presently my soul grew stronger: hesitating then no
  longer,
"Sir," said I, "or Madam, truly your forgiveness I implore;
But the fact is I was napping, and so gently you came
  rapping,
And so faintly you came tapping, tapping at my chamber door,
That I scarce was sure I heard you" — here I opened
  wide the door —
    Darkness there and nothing more.

Deep into that darkness peering, long I stood there,
  wondering, fearing,
Doubting, dreaming dreams no mortal ever dared to
  dream before;
But the silence was unbroken, and the stillness gave no
  token,
And the only word there spoken was the whispered
  word "Lenore!"
This I whispered, and an echo murmured back the
  word "Lenore!"
    Merely this and nothing more.

Back into the chamber turning, all my soul within me
  burning,
Soon again I heard a tapping, somewhat louder than
  before.
"Surely," said I, "surely that is something at my window lattice;
Let me see, then, what thereat is, and this mystery
  explore —
Let my heart be still a moment and this mystery explore —
    'Tis the wind and nothing more."

Open here I flung the shutter, when, with many a flirt and flutter,

In there stepped a stately Raven of the saintly days of yore.

Not the least obeisance made he, not a minute stopped or stayed he,

But with mien of lord or lady perched above my chamber door —

Perched upon a bust of Pallas just above my chamber door —

    Perched and sat, and nothing more.

Then, this ebony bird beguiling my sad fancy into smiling

By the grave and stern decorum of the countenance it wore,

"Though thy crest be shorn and shaven, thou," I said, "art sure no craven,

Ghastly, grim, and ancient Raven, wandering from the nightly shore:

Tell me what thy lordly name is on the night's Plutonian shore!"

    Quoth the Raven, "Nevermore."

Much I marveled this ungainly fowl to hear discourse so plainly,

Though its answer little meaning, little relevancy bore;

For we cannot help agreeing that no living human being

Ever yet was blessed with seeing bird above his chamber door —

Bird or beast upon the sculptured bust above his chamber door —

    With such name as "Nevermore."

But the Raven, sitting lonely on the placid bust, spoke only
That one word, as if his soul in that one word he did outpour.
Nothing further then he uttered, not a feather then he fluttered;
Till I scarcely more than muttered, "Other friends have flown before:
On the morrow he will leave me, as my hopes have flown before."
        Then the bird said, "Nevermore."

Startled at the stillness broken by reply so aptly spoken,
"Doubtless," said I, "what it utters is its only stock and store,
Caught from some unhappy master whom unmerciful Disaster
Followed fast and followed faster till his songs one burden bore,
Till the dirges of his hope that melancholy burden bore
        Of 'Never — nevermore.' "

But the Raven still beguiling my sad fancy into smiling,
Straight I wheeled a cushioned seat in front of bird and bust and door;
Then, upon the velvet sinking, I betook myself to linking
Fancy unto fancy, thinking what this ominous bird of yore,
What this grim, ungainly, ghastly, gaunt, and ominous bird of yore
        Meant in croaking "Nevermore."

This I sat engaged in guessing, but no syllable express-
ing
To the fowl, whose fiery eyes now burned into my
bosom's core;
This and more I sat divining, with my head at ease
reclining
On the cushion's velvet lining that the lamplight
gloated o'er,
But whose velvet-violet lining with the lamplight gloat-
ing o'er,
    She shall press, ah, nevermore!

Then, methought, the air grew denser, perfumed from
an unseen censer
Swung by seraphim whose foot-falls tinkled on the
tufted floor.
"Wretch," I cried, "thy God hath lent thee — by these
angels he hath sent thee
Respite — respite and nepenthe from thy memories of
Lenore!
Quaff, oh quaff this kind nepenthe, and forget this lost
Lenore!"
    Quoth the Raven, "Nevermore."

"Prophet!" said I, "thing of evil! prophet still, if bird
or devil!
Whether Tempter sent, or whether tempest tossed thee
here ashore,
Desolate yet all undaunted, on this desert land en-
chanted —
On this home by Horror haunted — tell me truly, I
implore:
Is there — is there balm in Gilead? — tell me — tell me,
I implore!"

Quoth the Raven, "Nevermore."

"Prophet!" said I, "thing of evil — prophet still, if bird
   or devil!
By that Heaven that bends above us, by that God we
   both adore,
Tell this soul with sorrow laden if, within the distant
   Aidenn,
It shall clasp a sainted maiden whom the angels name
   Lenore:
Clasp a rare and radiant maiden whom the angels name
   Lenore!"
   Quoth the Raven, "Nevermore."

"Be that word our sign of parting, bird or fiend!" I
   shrieked, upstarting:
"Get thee back into the tempest and the Night's Plutonian shore!
Leave no black plume as a token of that lie thy soul
   hath spoken!
Leave my loneliness unbroken! quit the bust above my
   door!
Take thy beak from out my heart, and take thy form
   from off my door!"
   Quoth the Raven, "Nevermore."

And the Raven, never flitting, still is sitting, *still* is
   sitting
On the pallid bust of Pallas just above my chamber
   door;
And his eyes have all the seeming of a demon's that is
   dreaming,
And the lamp-light o'er him streaming throws his
   shadow on the floor;
And my soul from out that shadow that lies floating on
   the floor
   Shall be lifted — nevermore!

Edgar Allan Poe

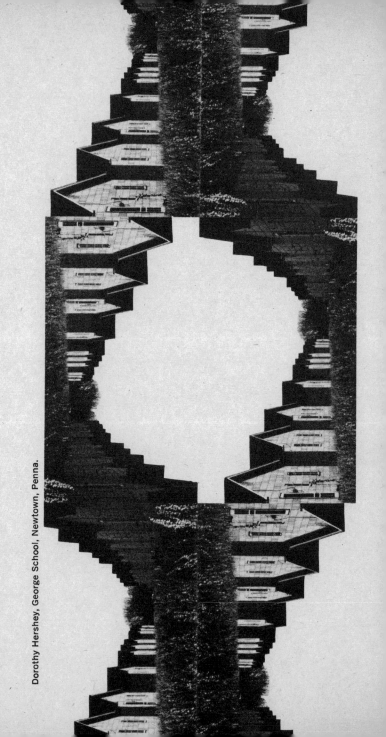

Dorothy Hershey, George School, Newtown, Penna.

VII
Riddles to Unriddle

NANCY ETTICOAT

Little Nancy Etticoat
With a white petticoat,
And a red nose;
She has no feet or hands,
The longer she stands
The shorter she grows.

BLIND VEGETABLE

An underground grower, blind and a common brown;
Got a misshapen look, it's nudged where it could;
Simple as soil yet crowded as earth with all.

Richard Wilbur

SPINNER

With six small diamonds for his eyes
He walks upon the summer skies,
Drawing from his silken blouse
The lacework of his dwelling house.

Robert P. Tristram Coffin

ONE GUESS

He has dust in his eyes and a fan for a wing,
A leg akimbo with which he can sing,
And a mouthful of dye stuff instead of a sting.

Robert Frost

LIVING TENDERLY

My body a rounded stone
with a pattern of smooth seams.
My head a short snake,
retractive, projective.
My legs come out of their sleeves
or shrink within,
and so does my chin.
My eyelids are quick clamps.

My back is my roof.
I am always at home.
I travel where my house walks.
It is a smooth stone.
It floats within the lake,
or rests in the dust.
My flesh lives tenderly
inside its bone.

May Swenson

AT BREAKFAST

Not quite
spherical
White
Oddly closed
And without a lid

A smooth miracle
here in my hand
Has it slid
from my sleeve?

The shape
of this box
keels me oval
Heels feel
its bottom
Nape knocks
its top

Seated
like a foetus
I look for
the dream-seam

What's inside?
A sun?
Off with its head
though it hasn't any
or is all head no body
a
One

Neatly
the knife scalps it
I scoop out
the braincap
soft
sweetly shuddering

Mooncream
this could be
Spoon
laps the larger
crescent
loosens a gilded
nucleus
from warm pap
A lyrical food

Opened
a seamless miracle
Ate a sun-germ
Good

May Swenson

I LIKE TO SEE IT LAP THE MILES

I like to see it lap the miles,
And lick the valleys up,
And stop to feed itself at tanks;
And then, prodigious, step

Around a pile of mountains,
And, supercilious, peer
In shanties by the sides of roads;
And then a quarry pare

To fit its sides, and crawl between,
Complaining all the while
In horrid, hooting stanza;
Then chase itself down hill

And neigh like Boanerges;
Then, punctual as a star,
Stop — docile and omnipotent —
At its own stable door.

Emily Dickinson

O WHERE ARE YOU GOING

"O where are you going?" said reader to rider,
"That valley is fatal when furnaces burn,
Yonder's the midden whose odours will madden,
That gap is the grave where the tall return."

"O do you imagine," said fearer to farer,
"That dusk will delay on your path to the pass,
Your diligent looking discover the lacking
Your footsteps feel from granite to grass?"

"O what was that bird," said horror to hearer,
"Did you see that shape in the twisted trees?
Behind you swiftly the figure comes softly,
The spot on your skin is a shocking disease?"

"Out of this house" — said rider to reader,
"Yours never will" — said farer to fearer,
"They're looking for you" — said hearer to horror,
As he left them there, as he left them there.

W. H. Auden

STUDENT NOTES

Group One

Fifteen   *Seventeenth:* 17th Street.

A Peck of Gold   Frost's birthplace (in 1874) and his home for his first ten years was San Francisco, where he often heard talk of the Forty-niners and the Gold Rush.

from **Running**   *keds:* sneakers, tennis shoes.

Digging for China   *patens* (line 23): a shallow dish used for bread in the communion service; here the sense suggests that they are the shimmering flat lights of dizziness.

Incident   This happened in 1911; Cullen was born in 1903.

The Blue-Tail Fly   This is an authentic American Negro minstrel song of the 1840's. It more than hints of the way black slaves felt about their masters.

The Day Time Began   The poet, U.S. Senator from
Minnesota, was among the
leading candidates for the
Presidency in 1968.

The Pardon   When Wilbur read this poem in public
in 1961 he remarked that for a long
time he had been embarrassed to read
it because it was true. He added that
the dream had come to him when he
was thirty — two decades after the
death of his dog.

My Lost Youth   *the beautiful town:* Portland, Maine,
Longfellow's birthplace in 1807. *"A
boy's will is the wind's will, . . ."*:
this famous refrain is Longfellow's
translation of a Lapland folksong
from Herder's German anthology of
folk-poetry:

Knabenwille ist Windeswille,
Jünglings Gedanken lange Gedanken.

Group Two

The Runaway   *a little Morgan:* a small horse first
bred in Vermont not many miles
from the poet's farm in Ripton.

Old Blue   This elegy to the Southern hound dog is
a folk song of the old Southwest, where
a good hunting dog put meat on the table

in lean years and fat. Old Blue is regarded quite simply as a member of the family.

Bobwhite This bird, one of the North American quails, is so named because its call sounds as though it were saying "bobwhite."

Group Three

Localities The mining towns the poet "never saw" are in Colorado; the places he knows — the Pecatonica River near Freeport and the Cedar Fork Creek — are all in Illinois. The poet was born and grew up in Galesburg among the children of Swedish immigrant parents like his own.

Chicago This was the title poem of Sandburg's first book, published in 1916.

Meeting-House Hill The church and city square are in Dorchester, overlooking Boston Harbor and Massachusetts Bay.

Building the Fire From *Snow-Bound*, which Whittier wrote in 1865. The setting, his family homestead in Amesbury, Mass., has been preserved as it was when he was a boy, and is open to the public.

The Ship-Builders	*drive the treenails:* the pins of hard wood used in fastening ship timbers. *no groaning cargo of despair:* slaves.
The Bishop of Atlanta: Ray Charles	Julian Bond, thrice elected to a seat in the Georgia House of Representatives but prevented from taking it by members who objected to his statements about the war in Viet Nam, was finally seated after the U.S. Supreme Court unanimously ruled that the Georgia House had erred. At the 1968 Democratic National Convention he was nominated for Vice-President, but withdrew his name from consideration because of his age. He was born in 1940 in Nashville.
Kansas	In the spring of 1912 Lindsay set out from his home in Springfield, Illinois, on a walking trip to the Pacific Coast. The late summer weeks of the wheat harvest he spent in Kansas.
Driving Toward the Lac Qui Parle River	The river of the title is literally the "lake that speaks."
For the Grave of Daniel Boone	The grave and monument are at Frankfort, Kentucky.

Old Ironsides The title is the nickname given to the U.S. frigate *Constitution*, best remembered for her victory over the British man-of-war *Guerrière* in the War of 1812. When in 1828 the Navy Department gave orders that she was to be dismantled, Holmes, then a young medical student, responded by writing the poem. Later the public subscribed enough money to repair the ship, and it is now a national monument at the Charlestown, Mass., Navy Yard.

O Captain! My Captain! Walt Whitman wrote the poem in 1865, the year of Lincoln's assassination.

Down in Dallas The shooting of President Kennedy occurred on Nov. 22, 1963. An earlier version of this ballad was published in an anthology of poems about President Kennedy, by various poets, *Of Poetry and Power*, Basic Books, N.Y.

Elegy for J. F. K. Auden collaborated with the composer Igor Stravinsky, supplying these words to be sung by solo voice with orchestral accompaniment. The elegy has been recorded. An account of the collaboration is given in *Themes and Episodes* by Igor Stravinsky and Robert Craft, Alfred A. Knopf, N. Y., 1966, pp. 56–9.

Granite and Steel

The poet's own notes: See *Brooklyn Bridge: Fact and Symbol*, by Alan Trachtenberg, Oxford University Press, N.Y., 1965. *Caged Circe*: See Meyer Berger's story of a young reporter who in the 1870's was unaccountably drawn to climb one of the cables to the top of the bridge's Manhattan tower, became spellbound, couldn't come down, and cried for help; none came till morning. *O catenary curve:* The curve formed by a rope or cable hanging freely between two fixed points of support. "Engineering problems of the greatest strength, greatest economy, greatest safety . . . are all solved by the same curve," John Roebling said. (Trachtenberg, p. 69.) *when darkness fell without a cause:* alludes to the great blackout of 1966 when electric power failed.

After living for many years in Brooklyn Heights, Marianne Moore in the mid-1960's moved across the Bridge to Manhattan.

Group Four

Indians on the Maine Coast

One early settler's remembrance of Indians in their summer encamp-

ments on the shores of Somes Pond,
Mt. Desert Island, around 1840.

The Indian Burying Ground	Philip Freneau (1752–1832) was the first poet to recognize the culture of the Indian as a distinctive part of the American heritage.
Hiawatha's Wedding Feast	From *The Song of Hiawatha*, first published in 1855. Glossary of proper names, with accents:
Pau-Puk-Keewis	(Pau-Puk-Kee´ wis) the handsome Yenadizze, the Storm-Fool.
Chibiabos	(Chibia´ bos) a musician; friend of Hiawatha; ruler in the land of the spirits.
Iagoo	(Ia´ goo) a great boaster and storyteller.
Nokomis	(Noko´ mis) grandmother of Hiawatha; mother of Wenonah.
Nahma	(Nah ma) the sturgeon.
Maskenozha	(Maskeno´ zha) the pike.
Yenadizze	(Yenadiz´ ze) an idler and gambler, an Indian dandy.
Nagow Wudjoo	(Na´ gow Wudj´ oo) the Sand Dunes of Lake Superior.
A Missouri Traveller Writes Home: 1830	In this poem the past is vividly recreated more than a hundred years after the events it describes. Robert Bly was born in 1926 in Madison, Minnesota, and after periods of study in the East and in

Iowa, he again lives there. He writes out of an intimate knowledge of the Mississippi and Missouri River country and of the history of the Western frontier.

At the Klamath Berry Festival

The annual harvest celebration held at Klamath in Southern Oregon, near the Klamath Indian Reservation.

The Moccasins of an Old Man

This and the three following poems were written by students at the Institute of American Indian Arts in Santa Fe, New Mexico. Ramona Carden is a member of the Colville tribe. She attended college in Washington State, where she received her M.A. She is married to a lawyer in Berkeley, California, and teaches in a school there.

Grandfather

Shirley Crawford belongs to the Kalistel tribe.

Uncertain Admission

Frances Bazil is Coeur d'Alene. She is now in her early 20's.

Battle Won Is Lost

Phil George, Nez Perce, was brought up by his grandmother in Wallowa, Washington. He was trained as a dental technician and spent two years in Viet Nam.

Ballad of Ira Hayes

The folk musician Peter La Farge comes from Fountain, Colorado, where he was raised as a cowboy. His tribe, the Nargasets, was wiped out, and he was adopted by the Tewa Tribe of the Hopi Nation, whose reservation is near Santa Fe. Peter went to Korea and returned to sing and ride rodeo. From then on he concentrated entirely on the folk field, and recorded many of his songs of the Indians on Folkways-Scholastic discs. La Farge died in 1965.

The Senecas

The long history of the steady erosion of Indian lands, and the struggles to resist their taking for roads and power projects is told in a number of books. See especially the *Indians of Americas*, by John Collier, Sr., New American Library, N.Y., 1963; and *Apologies to the Iroquois*, by Edmund Wilson, Farrar, Straus and Giroux, N.Y. 1960.

Group Five

A Caution to Everybody

auk: the great auk, a flightless black and white bird of the North Atlantic, which was hunted to extinction by seamen in 1844.

Once to Every Man and Nation

This fine hymn is an extract and abridgment of Lowell's poem "The Present Crisis," published in December 1845. The original poem, which was ninety lines in length, Lowell wrote in opposition to the terms for the annexation of Texas, terms which threatened a continuation of slavery in that state. However, Lowell never referred explicitly to Texas in the poem, a fact that has greatly extended its meaning and life.

To David, about His Education

excluded middle: a term in logic.

A Soldier

Frost wrote this sonnet on the death of his friend Edward Thomas, the English poet who was killed in battle in World War I.

Group Six

The Purist

A purist, as this poem wittily defines the word, is a person who insists upon precise usage in language.

Lama

Nash added a footnote on the final line: "The

author's attention has been called to a type of conflagration known as the three-alarmer. Pooh."

Phizzog Sandburg's word is halfway between the slang form *phiz* (face) and the full word *physiognomy*.

archy and mehitabel Don Marquis's famous cockroach archy first broke into print in 1916 in the "Sun Dial" column that Marquis ran in the *New York Sun*. Over the years he printed several hundred poems all supposed to have been written by archy. *vers libre bard:* a poet who writes verse having great rhythmic freedom and variety, often without rhyme or any regular stanza form.

The Raven Written in 1845. The raven, Poe once explained, "is emblematical of mournful and never-ending remembrance." *Bust of Pallas:* the sculptured head of Pallas Athena, Greek goddess of wisdom; *swung by seraphim:* wafted by angels; *quaff this kind nepenthe:* drink this drug of forgetfulness of sorrow; *Plutonian:* Pluto ruled the lower world, the dark world of death; *Aidenn:* Eden.

Group Seven

Nancy Etticoat   *A lighted candle.* From Mother Goose.

Blind Vegetable   *A potato.* The opening three lines of a poem by Richard Wilbur entitled "Potato."

Spinner   *A spider.* The opening three lines of a poem by Robert P. Tristram Coffin entitled "Feats in the Air."

One Guess   *A grasshopper.*

Living Tenderly   *A turtle.*

At Breakfast   *An egg.*

I Like to See it Lap the Miles   *A railway train.* Emily Dickinson wrote the poem in 1862, a few years after the first railway train ran to Amherst, Mass., from Belchertown, three cars drawn by a little steam locomotive, that made the twenty-mile run in fifty-five minutes. *Boanerges:* (Mark 3:17) sons of thunder.

O Where Are You Going?   The word *he* in the last line of the poem is the main clue: the rider, the farer, and the hearer are one person, faced by three challengers — his inner fears.

INDEX OF POEMS AND POETS